Contents

Introduction 3

Features 4

Unit 1: Life Science

Lesson 1: Science Tools 6

Content Vocabulary: chart, control, experiment, graph, law, model, scientist, theory

Academic Vocabulary: hypothesis, results

Lesson 2: Living Things 14

Content Vocabulary: adapt, bacteria, cell, classify, nucleus, reproduce, simple, species

Academic Vocabulary: divide, form

Lesson 3: Plants and Funguses 22

Content Vocabulary: fungus, grain, leaf, photosynthesis, root, seedling, sprout, stem

Academic Vocabulary: compare, notice

Lesson 4: Animals 30

Content Vocabulary: amphibian, dinosaur, embryo, hatch, mammal, ovary, reptile, vertebrate

Academic Vocabulary: develop, identify

Lesson 5: The Food Web 38

Content Vocabulary: consume, cycle, decay, energy, nutrients, produce, relationship, role

Academic Vocabulary: cause, example

Lesson 6: Ecosystems 46

Content Vocabulary: community, desert, ecosystem, environment, forest, habitat, population, tropical

Academic Vocabulary: examine, method

Unit 2: Earth Science

Lesson 7: Inside the Earth 54

Content Vocabulary: carbon, core, crust, fossil, mantle, mineral, nitrogen, oxygen

Academic Vocabulary: conduct, record

Vocabulary: Science, SV 9781419034992

Contents, *continued*

Lesson 8: The Changing Earth 62

Content Vocabulary: continent, earthquake, erosion, glacier, lava, sediment, surface, volcano

Academic Vocabulary: effect, recognize

Lesson 9: Space 70

Content Vocabulary: axis, lunar, orbit, phase, planet, revolve, satellite, solar

Academic Vocabulary: explore, measure

Lesson 10: Weather 78

Content Vocabulary: atmosphere, climate, evaporation, front, humidity, pressure, temperature, thermometer

Academic Vocabulary: label, predict

Lesson 11: The Earth's Resources 86

Content Vocabulary: conserve, deposit, enrich, extract, pollution, recycle, reduce, reusable

Academic Vocabulary: communicate, purpose

Unit 3: Physical Science

Lesson 12: Matter 94

Content Vocabulary: atom, density, gas, liquid, mass, matter, solid, volume

Academic Vocabulary: order, general

Lesson 13: Energy 102

Content Vocabulary: battery, circuit, conduction, current, electricity, heat, potential, static

Academic Vocabulary: design, figure

Lesson 14: Forces and Motion 110

Content Vocabulary: force, friction, gravity, lever, magnet, motion, poles, position

Academic Vocabulary: apply, instructions

Lesson 15: Sound and Light 118

Content Vocabulary: absorb, lens, pitch, prism, ray, reflect, vibrate, visible

Academic Vocabulary: include, prove

Answer Key 126

Introduction

Building a strong academic and content vocabulary is the key to success in science and social studies. Current reading research indicates that vocabulary is the major factor in improving comprehension. Research also shows that students benefit from a multi-strategy approach that exposes students to vocabulary in a variety of contexts. *Vocabulary in the Content Areas* is designed to supplement basal content-area textbooks by providing theme-based vocabulary study aligned to best-selling science and social studies textbooks and standards-based assessments.

> "Students learn new words better when they encounter them often and in various contexts. The more children see, hear, and work with specific words, the better they seem to learn them."
> *Put Reading First* (2001)

What is *Vocabulary in the Content Areas*?
- A developmental, research-based, interactive program designed to help students build a strong vocabulary foundation in science and social studies

How does *Vocabulary in the Content Areas* build a strong vocabulary foundation?
- Through explicit instruction, practice, and application of both content-area and academic vocabulary

What are content-area vocabulary and academic vocabulary?
- Content-area vocabulary refers to the subject-specific words that students need to understand content-area concepts. Examples: *amphibian, cellular, democracy, inflation*
- Academic vocabulary refers to the words and phrases that facilitate academic discourse and that are used across several content areas. Examples: *suggest, illustrate, analyze, diagram*

What skills and strategies does *Vocabulary in the Content Areas* target to help students with their content-area coursework?
- building associations with word anchors
- using word study skills such as affixes and roots
- using parts of speech and multiple meanings
- using synonyms and antonyms and comparisons and contrasts
- using specific context clues such as in-text definitions, examples, and descriptions

In what contexts does *Vocabulary in the Content Areas* teach vocabulary?
- reading
- listening
- writing
- speaking
- test practice

In sum, *Vocabulary in the Content Areas* helps students develop a robust academic vocabulary that supports them in
- comprehension of content-area textbooks
- meaningful participation in class discussion of content-area concepts
- production of articulate content-area writing
- success on content-area, standards-based assessments

Vocabulary: Science, SV 9781419034992

Features

Vocabulary Strategy and Reading Passages

Students practice the focus strategy with two high-interest reading passages. Suggestions for note taking and marking key information in the text also help students prepare for reading passages on standardized tests.

New Science Words and Other Useful Words

Student-friendly definitions are provided for content-area and academic vocabulary.

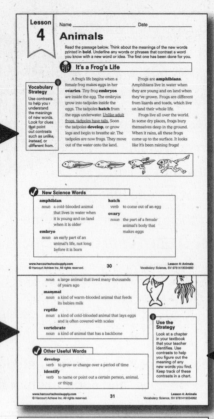

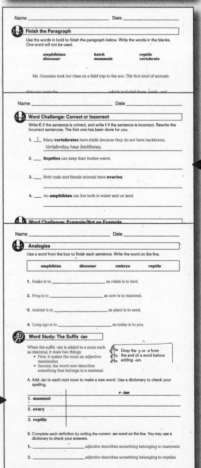

Use the Strategy

Students practice the focus strategy with their content-area textbooks.

Vocabulary Practice

Students receive ample practice with content and vocabulary through multiple encounters with words in a variety of contexts.

Word Study

Students both deepen their understanding of lesson words and increase their vocabulary acquisition through explicit instruction and practice with root words and affixes.

Features, continued

The Language of Testing

Students build confidence and master the language of tests through test-taking tips, strategies, and practice with the types of questions they will encounter on high-stakes tests.

* Answers for the multiple-choice questions in this section are included in the Answer Key for discussion purposes. It is up to teacher discretion to require students to answer these multiple-choice questions.

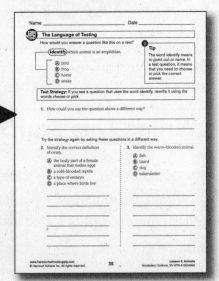

On Your Own

Students create their own understanding of content-area and academic vocabulary by answering questions that encourage thinking about the words in a variety of contexts.

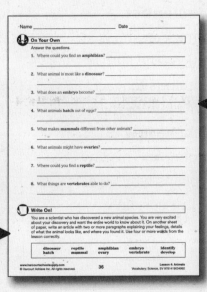

Write On!

A writing activity allows students to engage with the lesson vocabulary and concepts while also practicing key writing skills.

Assessment

Assessments for lessons provide an opportunity to monitor students' progress and give students practice answering questions in a standardized-test format.

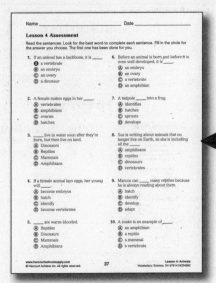

Name _____ Date _____

Science Tools

Read the passage below. Think about the meanings of the new words printed in **bold**. Underline any definitions that might help you figure out what these words mean. The first one has been done for you.

Who Writes This Stuff?

Vocabulary Strategy

Writers will often place definitions of new or difficult words near those words in text. Look for these definitions in the text to help you understand new words you find.

Your science textbook tells about plants, animals, the earth, and space. Did you ever wonder about the person who wrote your book?

The author of your textbook is probably a **scientist**. <u>A scientist is someone who is an expert in science.</u> The author decides what things to teach in the book. The author might decide to teach the **law** of motion, for example. This law is a rule that explains why objects always move in a certain way. The author also chooses which **theories** to include. A theory is a statement based on facts.

After the book is written, the author might decide to add photographs, drawings, and **charts**. A chart is a drawing that shows information in a way that is easy to understand.

It takes a lot of work to write a textbook. It might be even harder to learn without one, however!

New Science Words

chart
noun   a drawing that shows information in a way that makes it easy to understand

law
noun   a rule that says that things should always happen in a certain way

scientist
noun   a person who is an expert in science

theory
noun   a statement, based on facts, that explains why or how something happens

Vocabulary: Science, SV 9781419034992

Name _____ Date _____

Now read this passage and practice the vocabulary strategy again. Underline any definitions in the passage that help you figure out what the new words in **bold** mean.

 # Using the Scientific Method

The scientific method is a special way of testing ideas. In the first step you observe, or watch, something and ask questions about it. Then, you come up with a **hypothesis**. This is your guess about what you saw. The next step is to test your hypothesis by doing an **experiment**. An experiment is a test to find out if your hypothesis is correct.

You might use a **control** in your experiment. The **results** from the experiment, or what you discover, should be compared to the control. You may put your results in a **graph**, a drawing that helps you compare numbers.

Another kind of experiment might use a **model**. You use a model to show what you observed.

 ## More New Science Words

control

noun something in an experiment that everything else is compared to

verb to have power over something

experiment

noun a scientific test that is done to prove something or to find how one thing affects another

graph

noun a kind of drawing that compares numbers or amounts using lines, bars, or parts of a circle

model

noun a copy of something that shows its details, how it works, or what it is made of

"As the **graph** shows, my subject fell asleep during the **experiment**."

 ## Use the Strategy

Look at a chapter in your science textbook that your teacher identifies. Use definitions in the text to help you figure out the meanings of any new words you find.

 ## Other Useful Words

hypothesis

noun a guess or an idea that can be tested

results

noun what is discovered or learned from an experiment

Lesson 1: Science Tools
Vocabulary: Science, SV 9781419034992

Name _____ Date _____

Write a word from the box next to each clue. Then write the word made by the boxed letters. It tells you something you might find in a dream.

graph	model	control	law	hypothesis
experiment	chart	theory	scientist	

1. results are compared to this ___ ___ □ ___ ___ ___ ___

2. a test of an idea ___ ___ ___ □ ___ ___ ___ ___ ___

3. a drawing that compares numbers ___ ___ □ ___ ___ ___

4. an idea or guess ___ ___ ___ ___ □ ___ ___ ___ ___ ___ ___

5. a statement that explains □ ___ ___ ___ ___

6. a copy of something ___ □ ___ ___ ___

7. a rule ___ □ ___

8. a drawing that shows information ___ ___ ___ ___ □ ___

9. a science expert ___ ___ ___ □ ___ ___ ___ ___ ___

Answer: ___ ___ ___ ___ ___ ___ ___

Name _____ Date _____

Word Challenge: Correct or Incorrect

Write **C** if the sentence is correct, and write **I** if the sentence is incorrect. Rewrite the incorrect sentences. The first one has been done for you.

1. __C__ The **scientist** studied the way birds build their nests.

2. _____ Anya made a **hypothesis** to show how much her dog has grown.

   _____

3. _____ Liam drew a **graph** to compare the prices of new bicycles.

   _____

4. _____ Mateo wants to do an **experiment** to prove that he likes pizza.

   _____

Word Challenge: Which Word?

Think of a statement for each word below that gives a clue about its meaning. Write your statement next to the word. The first one has been done for you.

1. **experiment** _"I put ideas to the test."_ _____

2. **control** _____

3. **theory** _____

4. **results** _____

Name _____ Date _____

Extend the Meaning

Write the letter of the word or phrase that best completes each sentence.

1. A **theory** might _____.
   a. show how to do an experiment
   b. explain why flowers are certain colors
   c. tell the number of people living in a city

2. A **graph** might show _____.
   a. the amount of rainfall for each month of a year
   b. a drawing of a leaf
   c. the state capital

3. You might do an **experiment** to _____.
   a. find out what weeks have the sunniest days
   b. draw a map
   c. read a book before watching TV

4. A **law** might _____.
   a. show different places on a map
   b. explain why things fall to the ground
   c. compare two ideas to find out which one is better

Word Study: The *-ing* Ending

When the *-ing* ending is added to a noun such as *chart*, it does two things:
- First, it makes the noun a verb: *charting*.
- Second, it changes the word's meaning. The word now means "to make a chart."

chart (n.) a drawing that shows information in a way that makes it easy to understand
charting (v.) to make a drawing that shows information

Add *-ing* to the words below. Write definitions for the new words you made. Use a dictionary to check your spelling and definitions.

	+ *-ing*	Meaning
1. **experiment**		
2. **graph**		
3. **model**		
4. **control**		

Name _____ Date _____

The Language of Testing

How would you answer a question like this on a test?

All of the following statements are true

(except)

Ⓐ An experiment is a kind of test to prove something is true or false.

Ⓑ A scientist might study how light and water affect plant growth.

Ⓒ A theory and a hypothesis are the same.

Ⓓ A graph is one kind of chart.

Test Strategy: Read the question carefully so you are sure you understand it. Then, if it has the word *except* in it, ask the question in a different way. Remember that you are looking for the statement that is false.

1. How could you say the question above in a different way?

_____

_____

Try the strategy again by asking these questions in a different way.

2. Each of the following things is a type of chart except

Ⓐ graph

Ⓑ diagram

Ⓒ table

Ⓓ model

_____

_____

_____

_____

3. All of the following statements are false except

Ⓐ A graph is not a kind of chart.

Ⓑ Scientists know about science.

Ⓒ A model is also a theory.

Ⓓ A law is rarely followed.

_____

_____

_____

_____

Name _____ Date _____

 On Your Own

Answer the questions.

1. What information can you put in a **chart**? _____

_____

2. What would be a good **control** if you were testing how much water a plant needs?

_____

3. Describe an **experiment** you have done. _____

_____

4. What information can you place on a **graph**? _____

_____

5. Why do people make **laws**? _____

_____

6. How would you make a **model** of Earth? _____

_____

7. What are some things a **scientist** might study? _____

_____

8. What makes a **theory** different from a guess? _____

_____

 Write On!

Think about a career in science. On another sheet of paper, write a paragraph about what a scientist does. Tell whether or not you think it would be fun to be a scientist and why. Use four or more words from the lesson correctly.

chart	law	scientist	hypothesis	theory
graph	experiment	control	model	results

Vocabulary: Science, SV 9781419034992

Name _____ Date _____

Lesson 1 Assessment

Read the sentences. Look for the best word to complete each sentence. Fill in the circle for the answer you choose. The first one has been done for you.

1. Juan's father works for a lab. He is a _____.
   (A) model
   (B) hypothesis
   (C) scientist ●
   (D) control

2. John drew a _____ to show how many people at his school were born in another country.
   (A) theory
   (B) control
   (C) graph
   (D) model

3. They won't know the _____ of the election until tomorrow.
   (A) experiments
   (B) results
   (C) laws
   (D) controls

4. Ana hopes to test her _____ with an experiment.
   (A) control
   (B) graph
   (C) chart
   (D) hypothesis

5. Mark prepared a _____ for his class so that all the information would be easier to understand.
   (A) chart
   (B) law
   (C) hypothesis
   (D) control

6. Susana has an interesting _____ to explain the change in the local weather.
   (A) model
   (B) law
   (C) theory
   (D) control

7. The _____ in an experiment does not change.
   (A) model
   (B) scientist
   (C) chart
   (D) control

8. The _____ of gravity explains why things fall when you drop them.
   (A) law
   (B) result
   (C) control
   (D) model

9. Before scientists can prove anything, they have to do many _____.
   (A) models
   (B) experiments
   (C) theories
   (D) controls

10. Our teacher used a _____ of the human body to show us where the heart is.
    (A) chart
    (B) graph
    (C) model
    (D) control

Name _____ Date _____

Living Things

Read the passage below. Think about the meanings of the words printed in **bold**. Create connections between words you know and the new words. These will help you remember what the new words mean. Write these connections near the new words in the passage. The first one has been done for you.

The Scoop on Cells

building blocks

Vocabulary Strategy

Create connections between things you know and new words to "anchor" your understanding of new words. You can use a Word Anchor chart to help you create connections.

What's the big deal about **cells**? Cells are living building blocks. All living things are made of cells. Some plants and animals only have one cell. Others have millions and millions of cells. Scientists believe the human body has more than 10 trillion cells. That's 10,000,000,000,000 cells!

We can **classify**, or group, cells in many ways. For example, there are plant cells and animal cells. We can also classify cells by where they are in the body. There are nerve, bone, skin, and muscle cells.

The center of the cell is the **nucleus**. It's like the cell's brain. It holds all of the information about the plant or animal that the cell belongs to. If you could read the information in the nucleus, you would know the **species**, or special kind of plant or animal that the cell comes from.

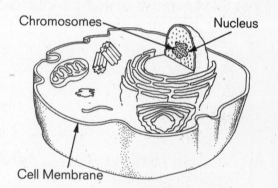

Chromosomes

Nucleus

Cell Membrane

Animal Cell

New Science Words

cell

noun   the smallest part of all living things

classify

verb   to sort things into groups by how they are alike

nucleus

noun   the central part of a cell

species

noun   a group of plants or animals that are alike in important ways

Name _____ Date _____

Now read this passage and practice the vocabulary strategy again. Write near the new words or mark in the passage any connections that will help you "anchor" the meaning of the new words.

 ## It Can Make You Sick!

Bacteria are among the smallest of all living things. They are **simple** creatures, made of a single cell. Some bacteria are helpful. Other bacteria can cause sickness and disease.

A person becomes sick when certain kinds of bacteria **reproduce**. The bacteria **divide** or split to make copies of themselves. Sometimes these bacteria reproduce very quickly. They can **form** or make a large army of bacteria in no time

at all. Bacteria give off a poison that the body cannot fight. When this happens, people take medicines to kill the bacteria. Some bacteria have started to **adapt** to the medicines, however. The bacteria change so that the medicine no longer works.

You have millions of different bacteria living on or in your body. The best way to protect yourself from sickness is to wash your hands often.

 ### More New Science Words

adapt
verb   to change to fit into a new or different situation

bacteria
noun   very tiny living things that can either be helpful or cause disease

reproduce
verb   to make a copy of something or to produce young

simple
adjective   having few parts or details

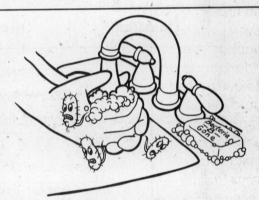

"I hate it when she does that!"

Use the Strategy

Look at a chapter in your science textbook that your teacher identifies. Use connections to help you anchor the meaning of any new words you find.

 ### Other Useful Words

divide
verb   to split into two or more parts

form
verb   to make something

Lesson 2: Living Things
Vocabulary: Science, SV 9781419034992

Name _____ Date _____

Finish the Sentence

Use a word from the box to finish each sentence. Write the correct word on the line.

adapt	cells	reproduce	simple

1. Some animals _____ to living in the snow by growing white fur.

2. When animals _____, they have babies.

3. The teacher told us that bacteria were _____ one-celled animals.

4. Every living thing is made of _____.

classified	divide	form	nucleus

5. After the field trip, we _____ the different shells we had

   collected by their size and shape.

6. The _____ controls all of the actions of a cell.

7. Our teacher asked us to _____ a line to go into the museum.

8. We had to _____ the two cookies so all four of us could

   have some.

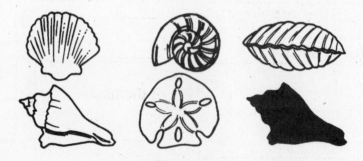

Name _____ Date _____

Word Challenge: Finish the Idea

Read the incomplete sentences below. Write an ending for each. The first one has been done for you.

1. Bears and deer are different **species** because _they are different from one another._

2. Some people think all **bacteria** are bad because _____

_____

3. A **nucleus** is important because _____

_____

4. **Cells** are called the building blocks of life because _____

_____

Word Challenge: What's Your Answer?

Read each question and write an answer on the line. Answer the questions in complete sentences. The first one has been done for you.

1. Where could you find the **nucleus** of a cell? _The nucleus is_

usually in the center of the cell.

2. Why might an animal have to **adapt**? _____

_____

3. What is a **simple** plant? _____

_____

4. How do bacteria **form** copies of themselves? _____

_____

Lesson 2: Living Things
Vocabulary: Science, SV 9781419034992

Name _____ Date _____

Extend the Meaning

Write the letter of the word or phrase that best completes the sentence.

1. For our science project, we had to _____ each of the animals by its species.

    a. **bacteria**   b. **nucleus**   c. **reproduce**   d. **classify**

2. The medicine didn't work because the bacteria had _____ to it.

    a. **nucleus**   b. **classified**   c. **adapted**   d. **simple**

3. _____ or one-celled plants can reproduce and make new plants in just a few weeks.

    a. **Simple**   b. **Species**   c. **Divided**   d. **Classified**

4. The _____ is part of a cell and is usually seen near the center.

    a. **bacteria**   b. **nucleus**   c. **species**   d. **form**

Word Study: The Prefix *re-*

The prefix *re-* means "to do something again." When it is added to a verb such as *divide*, it changes the verb's meaning. The verb now means "to divide again."

divide (v.) to split into two or more parts
redivide (v.) to split into two or more parts again

A. Add *re-* to the following words. Then write a definition for each new word.

	+ *re-*	Meaning
1. **form**		
2. **classify**		
3. **produce**		

B. Complete each sentence with an *re-* word from the chart above.

1. Chickens _____ by laying eggs.

2. If a plan you form doesn't work, you will need to _____ it.

Name _____ Date _____

The Language of Testing

How would you answer a question like this on a test?

(**Which of the following**) explains the word *cell*?

- Ⓐ a way of sorting things that are alike
- Ⓑ plants or animals that are alike
- Ⓒ the smallest part of all living things
- Ⓓ basic and easy to understand

Tip

The phrase *which of the following* means that you have to choose one of the answers listed (A, B, C, or D) to answer the question.

Test Strategy: If the question has the phrase *which of the following* in it, ask the question in a different way. Start your restated question with *what, who,* or *where*.

1. How could you say the question above in a different way?

_____

_____

Try the strategy again by asking these questions in a different way.

2. Which of the following explains the meaning of *adapt*?

- Ⓐ to change
- Ⓑ to sort things that are alike into groups
- Ⓒ to copy or to produce young
- Ⓓ to make better

3. Which of the following is the definition of *species*?

- Ⓐ the central part of a cell
- Ⓑ the smallest part of a living thing
- Ⓒ sorting things into groups
- Ⓓ a group of plants or animals that are alike in certain ways

_____   _____

_____   _____

_____   _____

Name _____ Date _____

Answer the questions.

1. What are some things you would have to **adapt** to if you moved away? _____
   _____

2. How do **bacteria** make people sick? _____
   _____

3. What would you find inside of a **cell**? _____
   _____

4. What kinds of things can you **classify**? _____
   _____

5. Why is a **nucleus** important to a cell? _____
   _____

6. How could you **reproduce** your homework if you lost it? _____
   _____

7. Name something that is **simple** to do. _____
   _____

8. How are you like other members of your **species**? _____
   _____

Write On!

You are in charge of a school project to help people stay healthy. You will be creating posters to place in all of the washing and eating areas of your school. On another sheet of paper, write a paragraph that gives at least one reason why germs are dangerous and four things that students and teachers can do to keep germs away. Use four or more words from the lesson correctly.

adapt	bacteria	divide	form	cell
classify	nucleus	reproduce	simple	species

Name _____ Date _____

Lesson 2 Assessment

Read the sentences. Look for the best word to complete each sentence. Fill in the circle for the answer you choose. The first one has been done for you.

1. These plants do not grow in this climate because they cannot _____.
   - Ⓐ divide
   - 🅑 adapt
   - Ⓒ form
   - Ⓓ classify

2. María _____ a committee to study air pollution around the school.
   - Ⓐ divided
   - Ⓑ reproduced
   - Ⓒ formed
   - Ⓓ adapted

3. Plants and animals are grouped according to their _____.
   - Ⓐ bacteria
   - Ⓑ forms
   - Ⓒ nucleus
   - Ⓓ species

4. Libraries need to _____ books so people know where to find them.
   - Ⓐ classify
   - Ⓑ reproduce
   - Ⓒ divide
   - Ⓓ adapt

5. A _____ organism may have one single cell.
   - Ⓐ form
   - Ⓑ cell
   - Ⓒ simple
   - Ⓓ nucleus

6. If plants and animals cannot _____, they will become extinct.
   - Ⓐ divide
   - Ⓑ form
   - Ⓒ classify
   - Ⓓ reproduce

7. _____ can make you sick.
   - Ⓐ Forms
   - Ⓑ Bacteria
   - Ⓒ Species
   - Ⓓ Cells

8. The _____ is at the center of a cell.
   - Ⓐ nucleus
   - Ⓑ species
   - Ⓒ form
   - Ⓓ bacteria

9. Our teacher _____ the class into four reading groups.
   - Ⓐ adapted
   - Ⓑ divided
   - Ⓒ reproduced
   - Ⓓ controlled

10. The smallest part of a living thing is a _____.
    - Ⓐ bacteria
    - Ⓑ species
    - Ⓒ cell
    - Ⓓ nucleus

Name _____ Date _____

Plants and Funguses

Read the passage below. Think about the meanings of the new words printed in **bold**. Underline any examples or descriptions you find that might help you figure out the meaning of these words. The first one has been done for you.

Getting Ready for Spring

Vocabulary Strategy

Sometimes writers give examples and descriptions to explain hard words and ideas. Look for clues, like *example*, *like*, or *such as*. Look for pictures that show what a new word means, too.

Many people who have gardens plant seeds in winter. They plant them in pots that they keep inside by a window. The seeds soon begin to **sprout** and grow. With enough light and water, the **sprouts** grow out of the seed and up through the dirt. These sprouts look like thin green threads. As the sprouts grow, they become **seedlings**. These young plants are tiny, but they usually have a **leaf** or two.

Photosynthesis happens inside the green leaves. Just like food is turned into energy in our bodies, photosynthesis turns water, air, and light into energy for the plant.

With care, the seedlings will grow into young plants. They can be moved outside when spring comes. The tiny sprouts from seeds will soon turn into a garden of flowers and vegetables.

New Science Words

leaf

noun   part of a plant that is flat, thin, and usually green

photosynthesis

noun   how green plants make food from sunlight, water, and air

seedling

noun   a young plant that has its first leaves

sprout

verb   to grow from a seed

noun   a very young plant just coming out of its seed

Name _____ Date _____

Now read this passage and practice the vocabulary strategy again. Underline the examples and descriptions in the passage. Draw an arrow from each to the word it describes.

Good Fungus – Bad Fungus

How about some **fungus** with your burger? Sounds gross, huh? But mushrooms are fungus. Many people enjoy eating mushrooms on burgers and steaks.

Unlike green plants, a fungus does not make its own food. Often, a fungus feeds on dead plants, a fallen tree, or leaves on the ground. The fungus breaks down the dead plants like a food chopper breaks up food. The tiny bits of dead plant material help make the soil rich.

Along with the good things funguses do, there are also some bad things. Wild mushrooms have poison in them. Another fungus grows under the ground on the **root** of the soybean plant. It grows like mold grows on bread. This fungus can kill the whole plant. Another fungus called "**stem** rust" attacks **grain**, such as wheat. This fungus grows onto a plant's stem, or the part of the plant that stands up out of the ground.

More New Science Words

fungus
noun a living thing that is like a plant but has no roots, leaves, or flowers

grain
noun a small, hard seed that is often eaten for food or a small piece of something, like sand

root
noun the part of a plant that grows under the ground

stem
noun the thin, upright part of a plant above ground

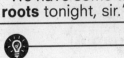

"We have some tasty **roots** tonight, sir."

Use the Strategy

Look at a chapter in your science textbook that your teacher identifies. Use examples, descriptions, and pictures in the text to help you figure out the meaning of any new words you find. You may want to draw pictures to help you remember what the new words mean.

Other Useful Words

compare
verb to look at two things to see how they are alike and different

notice
verb to see or to become aware of something

Name _____ Date _____

Matching

Finish the sentences in Group A with words from Group B. Write the letter of the word on the line.

Group A

1. The tall, thin _____ of the plant had

   several leaves growing on it.

2. The sunlight and air helped the grass

   carry out _____.

3. We moved the young _____ from the

   flower pot to the garden.

4. We watered the seeds, and soon they

   began to _____.

Group B

A. seedling
B. photosynthesis
C. stem
D. sprout

Group A

5. To get rid of the weed, we had to dig

   its _____ out of the ground.

6. The shape of the _____ told us it had

   fallen from an oak tree.

7. Rick likes to _____ prices before he

   buys anything.

8. When we passed the store, did you

   _____ if it was open?

Group B

E. roots
F. compare
G. leaf
H. notice

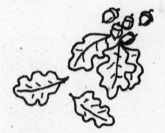

Vocabulary: Science, SV 9781419034992

Name _____   Date _____

Word Challenge: True or False

Write **T** next to each sentence that is true. Write **F** next to each sentence that is false. Rewrite the sentences that are false. The first one has been done for you.

1. _F_ **Sprouts** grow underground.

   Sprouts grow on top of the ground.
   _____

2. ____ The **root** is part of a plant that is flat, thin, and green.

   _____

3. ____ People eat **grains** such as wheat, corn, and oats in cereal.

   _____

4. ____ Plants make sunlight with **photosynthesis**.

   _____

Word Challenge: Which Word?

Think of a statement for each word below that gives a strong clue about its meaning. Write your statement next to the word. The first one has been done for you.

1. **fungus** _____"I eat dead leaves."_____

2. **root** _____

3. **sprout** _____

4. **seedling** _____

Name _____ Date _____

Finish the Idea

Finish each idea to make a complete sentence. Write your answer on the line.

1. I might look for a **fungus** in the forest because _____

_____.

2. I would **notice** a dog riding a motorcycle because _____

_____.

3. I would **compare** two different leaves by _____

_____.

4. I could make a seed **sprout** by _____

_____.

Word Study: The Suffix *-less*

When the suffix *–less* is added to a noun such as *stem*, it changes the word's meaning.
- First, it makes the noun an adjective: *stemless*.
- Second, it adds *without* to the meaning of the word.

stem (n.) the thin upright part of a plant
stemless (adj.) without a stem

A. Add *-less* to the following words. Then write a definition for each new word.

	+ *-less*	Meaning
1. **leaf**		
2. **root**		
3. **seed**		

B. Complete each sentence with a *-less* word from the chart above.

1. In fall, leaves fall from the trees. In winter, the trees are _____.

2. I like to eat grapes that do not have seeds. I like _____ grapes.

3. When a seed is planted, it doesn't have roots. It is _____.

The Language of Testing

How would you answer a question like this on a test?

What is a **characteristic** of a fungus?

A) It has roots.
B) It has flowers.
C) It grows in damp places.
D) It makes food through photosynthesis.

Tip

A *characteristic* of a thing is something that it usually has or does.

Test Strategy: If you see a question that uses the word *characteristic*, rewrite it to ask for something that is true about the subject of the question.

1. How could you say the question above in a different way?

_____

_____

Try the strategy again by asking these questions in a different way.

2. What is a characteristic of plants that use photosynthesis to make food?

A) They grow in dark, damp places.
B) They have green leaves.
C) They always grow in forests.
D) They are a type of fungus.

_____

_____

_____

_____

3. What is a characteristic of seedlings?

A) They have a long stem.
B) They have long roots.
C) They are still attached to a seed.
D) They give off spores.

_____

_____

_____

_____

Name _____ Date _____

On Your Own

Answer the questions.

1. Where would a **fungus** live? _____

_____

2. What things can you have a **grain** of? _____

_____

3. What does a **leaf** do for a plant? _____

_____

4. What do plants need for **photosynthesis** to happen? _____

_____

5. What things have **roots**? _____

_____

6. What does a **seedling** become? _____

_____

7. What will help a seed **sprout**? _____

_____

8. What does a **stem** do for a plant? _____

_____

Write On!

Pretend you are a seed. On another sheet of paper, write a letter home to let your family know that you are well and growing. Be sure to describe a plant's growing process. Use four or more words from the lesson correctly.

| compare | fungus | grain | leaf | seedling |
| root | sprout | notice | photosynthesis | stem |

Lesson 3: Plants and Funguses
Vocabulary: Science, SV 9781419034992

Lesson 3 Assessment

Read the sentences. Look for the best word to complete each sentence. Fill in the circle for the answer you choose. The first one has been done for you.

1. John's seeds did not _____ because he did not water them.
   Ⓐ compare
   Ⓑ stem
   Ⓒ notice
   ● sprout

2. _____ turns water, air, and light into energy for a plant.
   Ⓐ Comparing
   Ⓑ Photosynthesis
   Ⓒ A seedling
   Ⓓ A fungus

3. A _____ feeds on dead plants.
   Ⓐ stem
   Ⓑ grain
   Ⓒ fungus
   Ⓓ leaf

4. Sprouts grow into _____.
   Ⓐ seedlings
   Ⓑ leaves
   Ⓒ roots
   Ⓓ stems

5. Pam often _____ herself to her older sister.
   Ⓐ roots
   Ⓑ notices
   Ⓒ compares
   Ⓓ sprouts

6. Wheat, rice, and oats are all _____.
   Ⓐ fungi
   Ⓑ grains
   Ⓒ leaves
   Ⓓ stems

7. The _____ of a plant grows underground.
   Ⓐ leaf
   Ⓑ seedling
   Ⓒ stem
   Ⓓ root

8. Photosynthesis takes place within a _____.
   Ⓐ fungus
   Ⓑ leaf
   Ⓒ root
   Ⓓ grain

9. My mother likes flowers with long _____.
   Ⓐ seedlings
   Ⓑ grains
   Ⓒ stems
   Ⓓ roots

10. Miguel always _____ when our teacher is in a bad mood.
    Ⓐ notices
    Ⓑ stems
    Ⓒ compares
    Ⓓ sprouts

Animals

Read the passage below. Think about the meanings of the new words printed in **bold**. Underline any words or phrases that contrast a word you know with a new word or idea. The first one has been done for you.

It's a Frog's Life

Vocabulary Strategy

Use contrasts to help you understand the meanings of new words. Look for clues that point out contrasts such as *unlike*, *instead*, or *different from*.

A frog's life begins when a female frog makes eggs in her **ovaries**. Tiny frog **embryos** are inside the egg. The embryos grow into tadpoles inside the eggs. The tadpoles **hatch** from the eggs underwater. Unlike adult frogs, tadpoles have tails. Soon the tadpoles **develop**, or grow legs and begin to breathe air. The tadpoles are now frogs. They move out of the water onto the land.

Frogs are **amphibians**. Amphibians live in water when they are young and on land when they've grown. Frogs are different from lizards and toads, which live on land their whole life.

Frogs live all over the world. In some dry places, frogs bury themselves deep in the ground. When it rains, all these frogs come up to the surface. It looks like it's been raining frogs!

New Science Words

amphibian
noun a cold-blooded animal that lives in water when it is young and on land when it is older

embryo
noun an early part of an animal's life, not long before it is born

hatch
verb to come out of an egg

ovary
noun the part of a female animal's body that makes eggs

Now read this passage and practice the vocabulary strategy again. Underline any words or phrases that contrast something you know with a new word or idea. Look for clues like *unlike*, *instead*, or *different from*.

You're Getting Warmer

If you've ever held a lizard or a snake, you know that they aren't very warm. Lizards and snakes are **reptiles**. Reptiles are cold-blooded. Their bodies don't make their own heat so they need to warm themselves in the sun. Reptiles also are not furry like a rabbit. Instead, their bodies are often covered with scales.

Unlike reptiles, **mammals** such as rabbits are warm-blooded. Their bodies make heat. Also, instead of scales, most mammals have hair or fur. However, both reptiles and mammals are **vertebrates**. They have backbones, unlike some animals such as jellyfish.

The largest reptile that ever lived was the **dinosaur**. The largest *living* mammal scientists can **identify** is the blue whale. It can grow to be 100 feet long!

You shouldn't be afraid of us **vertebrates**.

But I have no backbone!

More New Science Words

dinosaur
noun   a large animal that lived many thousands of years ago

mammal
noun   a kind of warm-blooded animal that feeds its babies milk

reptile
noun   a kind of cold-blooded animal that lays eggs and is often covered with scales

vertebrate
noun   a kind of animal that has a backbone

Other Useful Words

develop
verb   to grow or change over a period of time

identify
verb   to name or point out a certain person, animal, or thing

Use the Strategy

Look at a chapter in your textbook that your teacher identifies. Use contrasts to help you figure out the meaning of any new words you find. Keep track of these contrasts in a chart.

Name _____   Date _____

Finish the Paragraph

Use the words in bold to finish the paragraph below. Write the words in the blanks.
One word will not be used.

amphibians   **hatch**   **reptile**
dinosaur   **mammals**   **vertebrate**

    Ms. Gonzales took her class on a field trip to the zoo. The first kind of animals

they saw were the _____, which included frogs, toads, and
                         1

salamanders. Next, the tour of the giant bird cage was really interesting. The class got

to see parrots and peacocks. As they left the cage, the class watched a baby robin

_____ from its egg. There were a lot of different snakes
          2

in the _____ house. One snake from South America was
               3

almost 20 feet long! The class had lunch near the area of the zoo where the

_____ lived. While they ate, they watched bears, elephants, and
          4

leopards. Later, as they were leaving the zoo, the class saw gigantic bones from a

_____ that roamed the earth millions of years ago.
          5

Lesson 4: Animals
Vocabulary: Science, SV 9781419034992

Name _____ Date _____

Word Challenge: Correct or Incorrect

Write **C** if the sentence is correct, and write **I** if the sentence is incorrect. Rewrite the incorrect sentences. The first one has been done for you.

1. __I__ Many **vertebrates** have shells because they do not have backbones.

   Vertebrates have backbones.

2. ____ **Reptiles** can keep their bodies warm.

3. ____ Both male and female animals have **ovaries**.

4. ____ An **amphibian** can live both in water and on land.

Word Challenge: Example/Not an Example

Think of things that are and are not examples of the words listed below. Write your responses in the chart. The first one has been done for you.

	Example	Not an Example
1. **dinosaur**	A Tyrannosaurus rex that lived a long time ago	A lizard in my yard
2. **develop**		
3. **identify**		
4. **hatch**		

Name _____ Date _____

 Analogies

Use a word from the box to finish each sentence. Write the word on the line.

amphibian	dinosaur	embryo	reptile

1. Snake is to _____ as robin is to bird.

2. Frog is to _____ as cow is to mammal.

3. Animal is to _____ as plant is to seed.

4. Long ago is to _____ as today is to you.

 Word Study: The Suffix -ian

When the suffix -ian is added to a noun such as *mammal,* it does two things:
- First, it makes the noun an adjective: *mammalian.*
- Second, the word now describes something that belongs to a mammal.

 Drop the -y or -e from the end of a word before adding -ian.

A. Add -ian to each root noun to make a new word. Use a dictionary to check your spelling.

	+ -ian
1. **mammal**	
2. **ovary**	
3. **reptile**	

B. Complete each definition by writing the correct -ian word on the line. You may use a dictionary to check your answers.

1. _____ *adjective* describes something belonging to mammals

2. _____ *adjective* describes something belonging to reptiles

Name _____ Date _____

The Language of Testing

How would you answer a question like this on a test?

Identify which animal is an amphibian.

- Ⓐ bird
- Ⓑ frog
- Ⓒ horse
- Ⓓ snake

Test Strategy: If you see a question that uses the word *identify*, rewrite it using the words *choose* or *pick*.

1. How could you say the question above a different way?

   _____

   _____

Try the strategy again by asking these questions in a different way.

2. Identify the correct definition of *ovary*.

   - Ⓐ the body part of a female animal that makes eggs
   - Ⓑ a cold-blooded reptile
   - Ⓒ a type of embryo
   - Ⓓ a place where birds live

3. Identify the warm-blooded animal.

   - Ⓐ fish
   - Ⓑ lizard
   - Ⓒ dog
   - Ⓓ salamander

Name _____ Date _____

Answer the questions.

1. Where could you find an **amphibian**? _____

   _____

2. What animal is most like a **dinosaur**? _____

   _____

3. What does an **embryo** become? _____

   _____

4. What animals **hatch** out of eggs? _____

   _____

5. What makes **mammals** different from other animals? _____

   _____

6. What animals might have **ovaries**? _____

   _____

7. Where could you find a **reptile**? _____

   _____

8. What things are **vertebrates** able to do? _____

   _____

Write On!

You are a scientist who has discovered a new animal species. You are very excited about your discovery and want the entire world to know about it. On another sheet of paper, write an article with two or more paragraphs explaining your feelings, details of what the animal looks like, and where you found it. Use four or more words from the lesson correctly.

dinosaur	reptile	amphibian	embryo	identify
hatch	mammal	ovary	vertebrate	develop

Vocabulary: Science, SV 9781419034992

Name _____ Date _____

Lesson 4 Assessment

Read the sentences. Look for the best word to complete each sentence. Fill in the circle for the answer you choose. The first one has been done for you.

1. If an animal has a backbone, it is _____.
   - Ⓐ a vertebrate
   - Ⓑ an embryo
   - Ⓒ an ovary
   - Ⓓ a dinosaur

2. A female makes eggs in her _____.
   - Ⓐ vertebrates
   - Ⓑ amphibians
   - Ⓒ ovaries
   - Ⓓ hatches

3. _____ live in water soon after they're born, but then live on land.
   - Ⓐ Dinosaurs
   - Ⓑ Reptiles
   - Ⓒ Mammals
   - Ⓓ Amphibians

4. If a female animal lays eggs, her young will _____.
   - Ⓐ become embryos
   - Ⓑ hatch
   - Ⓒ identify
   - Ⓓ become vertebrates

5. _____ are warm-blooded.
   - Ⓐ Reptiles
   - Ⓑ Dinosaurs
   - Ⓒ Mammals
   - Ⓓ Amphibians

6. Before an animal is born and before it is even well developed, it is _____.
   - Ⓐ an embryo
   - Ⓑ an ovary
   - Ⓒ a vertebrate
   - Ⓓ an amphibian

7. A tadpole _____ into a frog.
   - Ⓐ identifies
   - Ⓑ hatches
   - Ⓒ sprouts
   - Ⓓ develops

8. Sue is writing about animals that no longer live on Earth, so she is including all the _____.
   - Ⓐ amphibians
   - Ⓑ reptiles
   - Ⓒ dinosaurs
   - Ⓓ vertebrates

9. Marcos can _____ many reptiles because he is always reading about them.
   - Ⓐ hatch
   - Ⓑ identify
   - Ⓒ develop
   - Ⓓ adapt

10. A snake is an example of _____.
    - Ⓐ an amphibian
    - Ⓑ a reptile
    - Ⓒ a mammal
    - Ⓓ a vertebrate

Lesson 4: Animals
Vocabulary: Science, SV 9781419034992

The Food Web

Read the passage below. Think about the meanings of the new words printed in **bold**. Circle any any synonyms, or words that mean the same as the new words. Draw an arrow from each synonym to the new word it describes. The first one has been done for you.

In the Rain Forest

Vocabulary Strategy

Use synonyms, or words that mean about the same as the new words, to help you understand their meaning. Look for clues like the word *or* to help you find synonyms in a text.

The rain forests of South America hold thousands of species of plants and animals. There is a **relationship** among all of these living things in the rain forest. This relationship, or connection, makes the rain forest an interesting place to study. Every plant and animal has a special purpose, or **role**, in the food web of the rain forest.

The food web is like a big circle, or **cycle**. This cycle begins when the sun **produces**, or makes, light so that plants can grow. Sunlight provides **energy** for the plants. They draw strength from the sunlight. Animals get energy by eating the plants. Other animals get energy by eating these animals. When the plants and animals die, they rot and go back to the soil. Plants grow in the soil, finishing the cycle.

New Science Words

cycle
noun a string of things that happen over and over again in the same order

energy
noun the power or strength needed to do work or grow

produce
verb to make something or to make something happen

relationship
noun how one thing connects to or affects another

role
noun the job that someone or something has to do

38

Name _____ Date _____

Now read this passage and practice the vocabulary strategy again. Circle any synonyms and draw an arrow from each one to the new word it describes.

How to Make Compost

Many gardeners like to make compost. Compost is a mixture of dead plants and dirt. When dead plants break down they put **nutrients** back into the soil. Compost nutrients are a kind of plant food. Just like we eat food, plants **consume** or take in the nutrients in compost. Gardeners put compost in the flowerbeds and vegetable gardens to make the plants grow.

Compost is easy to make. All you need is some dead plant material. For **example**, fruits and vegetables are good for making compost. Place these items, or some grass and leaves, in a pile. Add a layer of dirt. Over time, keep adding plants and dirt in layers. When these things **decay**, or rot, they produce compost. Let the pile sit for six to seven months. Waiting this long will **cause** the compost to become richer. After a while, you'll have a fresh batch of compost!

"**Consume** faster! We need more compost!"

More New Science Words

consume
  verb   to eat, take in, or use up

decay
  verb   to rot or break down

nutrients
  noun   something that plants and animals
         need to stay strong and healthy

Other Useful Words

cause
  verb   to make something happen
  noun   the reason why something happens

example
  noun   something that can stand for a certain group

Use the Strategy

Look at a chapter in your science textbook that your teacher identifies. Use synonyms in the text to help you understand the meaning of any new words you find. Keep track of new words and their synonyms in a chart.

Name _____ Date _____

 Find the Word

Write a word from the box next to each clue. Then write the word made by the boxed letters. It tells you something you might say at dinnertime.

role	nutrients	energy	decay
cycle	relationship	consume	

1. something that happens again and again   __ __ __ ☐ __

2. an important job   __ __ __ ☐

3. these make you strong   __ __ ☐ __ __ __ __ __

4. to take something in   __ __ __ ☐ __ __ __

5. the power to do things   ☐ __ __ __ __ __

6. to rot   __ __ __ ☐ __

7. a connection   __ __ __ ☐ __ __ __ __ __ __ __

Answer: __ __ __ ' __   __ __ __ !

Lesson 5: The Food Web
Vocabulary: Science, SV 9781419034992

Name _____   Date _____

Word Challenge: Which Word?

Think of a statement for each word below that gives a strong clue about its meaning. Write your statement next to the word. The first one has been done for you.

1. **cause** _"I make things happen."_ _____

2. **example** _____

3. **energy** _____

4. **produce** _____

Word Challenge: What's Your Answer?

Read each question and write an answer on the line. Answer the questions in complete sentences. The first one has been done for you.

1. How do you **produce** a good homework assignment? _____
   I follow directions and write neatly. _____

2. How can you tell that something is **decaying**? _____
   _____

3. What foods do you **consume** every day? _____
   _____

4. What **relationships** do you have in your life? _____
   _____

Name _____ Date _____

Word Connections

In the spaces at the top of the wheel, write the words from the box that connect to the center word or idea. In the spaces at the bottom of the wheel, write the words that do not connect.

| cycle | decay | energy | nutrients | cause | example |

YES

X   consume   X

X

NO

Word Study: The Suffixes *-able* and *-ible*

When the suffix *-able* or *-ible* is added to a verb such as *consume*, it does two things:
- First, it makes the verb an adjective: *consumable*.
- Second, it changes the word's meaning. The word now describes something that can be eaten or used up.

> Drop the *-e* from the end of a word before adding *-able* or *-ible*.

A. Write each word's root verb and suffix. Use a dictionary if you need help.

	Root Word	**+ *-able* or *-ible* Suffix?**
1. **consumable**		
2. **producible**		

B. Complete each sentence with a word from the chart.

1. Bananas are _____ only in warm places.

2. Something we can eat or drink is _____ .

Name _____ Date _____

The Language of Testing

How would you answer a question like this on a test?

What is the **purpose of** nutrients?

- Ⓐ They provide moisture to plants.
- Ⓑ They help plants and animals grow.
- Ⓒ They help break down dead plants.
- Ⓓ They provide oxygen for the blood.

Tip

The word *purpose* can mean *reason* or *use*.

Test Strategy: If you see a question that uses the word *purpose*, rewrite it using the words *reason* or *use*.

1. How could you say the question above in a different way?

   _____

   _____

Try the strategy again by asking these questions in a different way.

2. What is the purpose of decomposition?

   - Ⓐ It breaks down dead matter.
   - Ⓑ It allows animals to feed off the dead plants.
   - Ⓒ Reproduction takes place there.
   - Ⓓ It creates a way for animals to adapt to changing climates.

   _____

   _____

   _____

3. What is the main purpose of photosynthesis?

   - Ⓐ to create oxygen
   - Ⓑ to use carbon dioxide
   - Ⓒ to produce energy for plants
   - Ⓓ to produce energy for animals

   _____

   _____

   _____

Name _____ Date _____

On Your Own

Answer the questions.

1. What things do you **consume**? _____

_____

2. Describe a **cycle** that is part of your life. _____

_____

3. What things might **decay**? _____

_____

4. What are some sources of **energy**? _____

_____

5. What **nutrients** do you get from vegetables? _____

_____

6. What things do plants **produce**? _____

_____

7. With whom do you have a close **relationship**? _____

_____

8. What is your **role** in your family? _____

_____

Write On!

You're a scientist and a space traveler. You've landed on a strange planet to watch how plants and animals live there. On another sheet of paper, write a paragraph describing a food web on this planet. Use four or more words from the lesson correctly.

consume	energy	produce	relationship	cycle
role	nutrients	decay	cause	example

Lesson 5: The Food Web
Vocabulary: Science, SV 9781419034992

Lesson 5 Assessment

Read the sentences. Look for the best word to complete each sentence. Fill in the circle for the answer you choose. The first one has been done for you.

1. Plants need _____ to stay strong.
   - Ⓐ examples
   - Ⓑ decay
   - **Ⓒ nutrients**
   - Ⓓ energy

2. Sunlight provides _____ for plants.
   - Ⓐ cycles
   - Ⓑ energy
   - Ⓒ relationships
   - Ⓓ roles

3. The sun _____ light that allows plants to grow.
   - Ⓐ produces
   - Ⓑ decays
   - Ⓒ cycles
   - Ⓓ consumes

4. A link is like a _____.
   - Ⓐ role
   - Ⓑ cycle
   - Ⓒ relationship
   - Ⓓ cause

5. After living things die, they _____.
   - Ⓐ produce
   - Ⓑ consume
   - Ⓒ become examples
   - Ⓓ decay

6. Poor soil _____ plants to become weak.
   - Ⓐ consumes
   - Ⓑ causes
   - Ⓒ decays
   - Ⓓ divides

7. In a food web, plants and animals play special _____.
   - Ⓐ roles
   - Ⓑ causes
   - Ⓒ cycles
   - Ⓓ nutrients

8. A robin is _____ of a bird.
   - Ⓐ a cause
   - Ⓑ a nutrient
   - Ⓒ an example
   - Ⓓ a cycle

9. Plants _____ nutrients in the soil.
   - Ⓐ cause
   - Ⓑ decay
   - Ⓒ produce
   - Ⓓ consume

10. _____ happen over and over.
    - Ⓐ Roles
    - Ⓑ Causes
    - Ⓒ Cycles
    - Ⓓ Examples

Lesson 5: The Food Web
Vocabulary: Science, SV 9781419034992

Name _____ Date _____

Ecosystems

Read the passage below. Think about the meaning of the words printed in **bold**. Underline any words that start with *eco-* or end with *-ity*. Write what you think each word means near it. Remember that *eco-* names a place in nature, and *-ity* names a way of being. The first one has been done for you.

Your Own Special World

Vocabulary Strategy

Use prefixes and suffixes you know to help you understand the meanings of new words.

system in nature

You can create your own world in a terrarium. A terrarium is actually a **habitat** in which small plants and animals can live together. It is like an **ecosystem** in a bottle!

To make a terrarium, you'll need a large glass or plastic bottle. Fill the bottom with a layer of small rocks or pebbles. Add potting soil for the next layer.

Next, choose the kind of **environment** you want. You could have a dry environment, like a desert. Or, you could have a warm and wet, or **tropical**, environment. Choose plants that grow well together in your environment. Place each plant in damp soil. Then put your terrarium in an area that gets a lot of light, but not too much.

Once you have the plants, you might want to add a toad or snail. Now you have your own **community** in a bottle.

New Science Words

community

noun   a group of plants, animals, or people living in the same area

ecosystem

noun   the plants, animals, and nonliving things in an area that have a relationship with one another

environment

noun   the natural world of land, sea, and air and the things that affect it

habitat

noun   the natural place where a plant or animal lives and grows

tropical

adjective   having to do with the tropics, a very hot and wet area of the earth

www.harcourtschoolsupply.com
46
Lesson 6: Ecosystems
Vocabulary: Science, SV 9781419034992

Name _____ Date _____

Now read this passage and look for prefixes or suffixes to help you understand the words in **bold**. Circle any words that end with *-al*, *-ation*, and *-ist*. Write what you think each circled word means next to it. Remember that *-al* names a connection, *-ation* names a process, and *-ist* names someone who does a certain thing.

The Gobi Desert

Most people think a **desert** is a very hot place. In fact, one of the earth's largest deserts is also its coldest. The summer temperature there is usually around 70°F. The winter temperature is usually an icy 10°F. That's hardly tropical weather! Welcome to China's Gobi desert.

The Gobi desert covers over a half-million square miles. The soil is dry and mostly rocky. Much of the Gobi gets less than ten inches of rain or snow a year. There are not many trees, so there are no **forests**. Instead, many different kinds of grasses grow in the Gobi desert.

Do you think you'd like to live in the Gobi desert? The **population** is small. Most people live around the edges of the desert where more rain falls. Other people move from place to place looking for water and food for their sheep and cattle. Scientists believe people have lived in the Gobi for thousands of years.

Tired of ice and snow, Pedro found the Gobi **desert** a nice change.

More New Science Words

desert
 noun   a dry area of land with few plants

forest
 noun   a large area of land where many trees grow close together

population
 noun   the number of plants, animals, or humans that live in a certain area

Use the Strategy

Look at a chapter in your science textbook that your teacher identifies. Use prefixes and suffixes you know to help you figure out the meanings of any new words you find.

Other Useful Words

examine
 verb   to look at or check something very carefully

method
 noun   a certain way of doing something

Name _____ Date _____

 The Right Word

Read each sentence. Look at the word or phrase that is underlined. Write one of the words from the box that means the same or almost the same as the underlined part of the sentence.

desert	population	tropical	examined

1. _____ The <u>number of people living in the area</u> had grown in the past two years.

2. _____ The doctor <u>studied</u> his patient carefully.

3. _____ We almost ran out of water as we traveled across the <u>hot, dry area</u>.

4. _____ After the cool weather, the <u>warm, wet</u> weather felt great.

environment	forest	habitat	method

5. _____ The tiger was pushed out of its <u>natural home</u> by new villages.

6. _____ Petra had a <u>certain way</u> for making a sandwich.

7. _____ During the hike, we walked through a <u>thick area of trees</u>.

8. _____ Everyone should work to keep the <u>air, land, and water we live in</u> clean.

Name _____ Date _____

Word Challenge: True or False

Write **T** next to each sentence that is true. Write **F** next to each sentence that is false. Rewrite each false sentence. The first one has been done for you.

1. __F__ A **tropical** climate is usually very cool and dry.

   A tropical climate is usually very warm and wet.
   _____

2. _____ Some scientists follow the **population** of dolphins.

   _____

3. _____ A **forest** has no trees and many wildflowers.

   _____

4. _____ The **habitat** of most fish is in a desert.

   _____

Word Challenge: What's Your Answer?

Read each question and write an answer on the line. Answer the questions with complete sentences. The first one has been done for you.

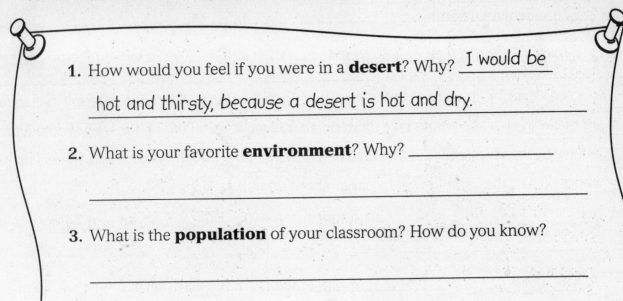

1. How would you feel if you were in a **desert**? Why? I would be
   hot and thirsty, because a desert is hot and dry.

2. What is your favorite **environment**? Why? _____

   _____

3. What is the **population** of your classroom? How do you know?

   _____

4. Who is an important member of your **community**? Why is he or she

   important? _____

Lesson 6: Ecosystems
Vocabulary: Science, SV 9781419034992

Name _____ Date _____

Analogies

Use a word from the box to finish each sentence. Write the word on the line.

desert	forest	examine	tropical

1. Ocean is to wet as _____ is to dry.

2. Book is to library as tree is to _____.

3. Heat is to _____ as cold is to arctic.

4. Eye is to _____ as ear is to listen.

Word Study: The Prefix *inter-*

When the prefix *inter-* is added to a noun such as *forest*, it changes the noun's meaning.

- First, it makes the noun an adjective: *interforest*.
- Second, it adds *between* or *among* to the word's meaning.

forest (n.) a large area of land where many trees grow close together
interforest (adj.) between or among forests

A. Circle the *inter-* words in the story.

Joanie and Kim were ready to go. They were leaving to do intercommunity science studies. An airplane would take them on an interecosystem trip. First, they would learn about the interforest flight of birds. Then they would study the interdesert travels of people. Then they would write a paper about what they learned.

B. Complete each sentence with an *inter-* word from the story.

1. The word _____ means "between deserts."

2. When birds fly between forests, their flight is _____.

3. Their _____ studies took Joanie and Kim to many places.

Name _____ Date _____

How would you answer a question like this on a test?

A large area in North Africa rarely receives any rainfall. What does this statement **suggest**?

Ⓐ It is probably a good place for farming.
Ⓑ It is probably a desert climate.
Ⓒ It is probably near mountains.
Ⓓ It is probably a tropical climate.

Tip
When *suggest* is used in a question, you should draw a conclusion about the information in the question.

Test Strategy: If you see a question that uses the word *suggest*, rewrite it so that it asks you what the information in the question probably means.

1. How could you say the question above in a different way?

_____

_____

Try the strategy again by asking these questions in a different way.

2. What does it suggest about an area if the population is growing quickly?

Ⓐ The area is a big city.
Ⓑ The weather is good.
Ⓒ People are attracted to something in the area.
Ⓓ The area had few people.

_____

_____

_____

_____

3. Many plants in an area are slowly dying. What does this suggest?

Ⓐ The ecosystem is in trouble.
Ⓑ The plants need a new habitat.
Ⓒ There isn't much soil.
Ⓓ There are too many animals.

_____

_____

_____

_____

Name _____ Date _____

 On Your Own

Answer the questions.

1. Describe a **community** that you belong to. _____

_____

2. What kinds of plants and animals live in a **desert**? _____

_____

3. What things does an **ecosystem** need to have? _____

_____

4. Describe the **environment** that you live in. _____

_____

5. What plants and animals would you find in a **forest**? _____

_____

6. What does an animal need in its **habitat**? _____

_____

7. What is the **population** of your town or city? _____

_____

8. What plants and animals could live in a **tropical** place? _____

_____

Write On!

An animal is in danger of losing its natural home because a fast-food restaurant is planned for the area. On another sheet of paper, write a letter to your newspaper telling why saving this animal's home is more important than building another fast-food restaurant. Use four or more words from the lesson in your letter.

forest	**population**	**community**	**examine**	**method**
desert	**ecosystem**	**environment**	**habitat**	**tropical**

Vocabulary: Science, SV 9781419034992

Name _____ Date _____

Lesson 6 Assessment

Read the sentences. Look for the best word to complete each sentence. Fill in the circle for the answer you choose. The first one has been done for you.

1. The special way you have of doing something is your _____.
   Ⓐ community
   Ⓑ ecosystem
   Ⓒ habitat
   Ⓓ method

2. A whale's _____ is the ocean.
   Ⓐ desert
   Ⓑ method
   Ⓒ habitat
   Ⓓ population

3. If you know how many people live in your town, you know its _____.
   Ⓐ environment
   Ⓑ population
   Ⓒ habitat
   Ⓓ ecosystem

4. _____ often provide wood for making paper and furniture.
   Ⓐ Ecosystems
   Ⓑ Deserts
   Ⓒ Forests
   Ⓓ Populations

5. If you like warm and wet weather, you'd be happy in _____.
   Ⓐ a tropical country
   Ⓑ a desert
   Ⓒ an ecosystem
   Ⓓ a community

6. Jamie works hard to help keep the city's _____ clean.
   Ⓐ population
   Ⓑ form
   Ⓒ methods
   Ⓓ environment

7. You and other things living in the same area form _____.
   Ⓐ a method
   Ⓑ a community
   Ⓒ a divide
   Ⓓ a forest

8. A city park can be _____.
   Ⓐ a community
   Ⓑ a population
   Ⓒ an ecosystem
   Ⓓ a method

9. Not many plants and animals live in _____.
   Ⓐ a tropical country
   Ⓑ a population
   Ⓒ a forest
   Ⓓ a desert

10. You need to _____ an animal's habitat to understand it.
    Ⓐ method
    Ⓑ form
    Ⓒ examine
    Ⓓ divide

Name _____ Date _____

Inside the Earth

Read the passage below. Think about the meanings of the new words printed in **bold**. Underline any examples or descriptions you find that might help you figure out what these words mean. The first one has been done for you.

Science Fact or Science Fiction?

Vocabulary Strategy

Look for examples and descriptions in a text to help you figure out the meanings of new words. Look for clues, like *example*, *like*, or *such as*. Look for pictures that show what a new word means, too.

Jules Verne was a writer who lived in the 1800s. His stories were filled with adventures that were based on science. Many of his books are still popular today. One of his books is *A Journey to the Center of the Earth*.

This book is about a scientist who travels under the earth's **crust**. <u>This crust is very much like the top crust on a pie.</u> The scientist believes he can reach the earth's **core**, which is like the core at the center of an apple. Instead, he finds an underground ocean. Today, scientists know that between the crust and core is a layer called the **mantle**. This mantle is made up of very hot rock, not water.

In the book, the scientist also meets dinosaurs. In the real world he would find only **fossils**, like the ones we see today in museums. Much of Jules Verne's science was more fiction than fact. However, he could still tell a great story.

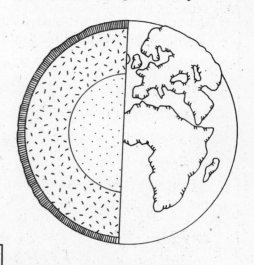

New Science Words

core

noun the very center part of the earth

crust

noun the outer layer of the earth

fossil

noun the parts of dead plants or animals that have turned into rock

mantle

noun the layer of the earth between the center and the outer crust

Name _____ Date _____

Now read this passage and practice the vocabulary strategy again. Underline examples and descriptions in the passage. Draw an arrow from each one to the new word it describes.

It's Elemental

Scientists have discovered 110 elements in the world. An element is made up completely of one thing. If you take it apart to its smallest, tiniest piece, every part of the element will be the same. Everything in the world is made up of those 110 elements.

Some elements like gold are worth a lot of money. Other elements like **oxygen** and **nitrogen** are as free as the air. In fact, they're part of the air you breathe.

Other elements are called **minerals**. These elements are hard and solid. Some minerals are dark like rock. Others are crystals that you can see through, almost like glass.

Carbon is a mineral that is sometimes like a rock and sometimes like a crystal. Coal and diamonds are both examples of carbon. We sometimes cook with coal and use it to heat our homes. We use diamonds to make jewelry.

 More New Science Words

carbon
  noun a material found in the earth that is necessary for life

mineral
  noun a nonliving material found in nature such as salt, iron, and silver

nitrogen
  noun a colorless material found in nature in the air and in the soil

oxygen
  noun a colorless material in the air that is needed by most life

"Well, a diamond is really just **carbon**!"

 Use the Strategy

Look at a chapter in your science textbook that your teacher identifies. Use examples, descriptions, and pictures to help you figure out the meaning of any new words you find.

 Other Useful Words

conduct
  verb to plan and do something

record
  verb to put information in writing
  noun information that has been saved

Name _____ Date _____

Finish the Sentence

Use a word from the box to finish each sentence. Write the correct word on the line.

core	fossil	mineral	oxygen

1. We found a _____ of an insect in the stone.

2. She hollowed out the center of the fruit down to its _____.

3. Animals need _____ to breathe.

4. Iron is a _____ that is found in nature.

crust	recorded	carbon	mantle

5. Eli's grandfather _____ their family history in a notebook.

6. The frozen lake had a _____ of ice on the top.

7. The wood burned down to a block of _____ that looked

   like coal.

8. Hot rock is in the _____ of the earth.

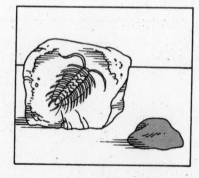

Word Challenge: Which Word?

Think of a statement for each word below that gives a clue about its meaning. Write your statement next to the word. The first one has been done for you.

1. **core** *"I am the center of the earth!"* _____

2. **carbon** _____

3. **fossil** _____

4. **nitrogen** _____

Word Challenge: Correct or Incorrect

Write **C** if the sentence is correct, and write **I** if the sentence is incorrect. Rewrite the incorrect sentences. The first one has been done for you.

1. __I__ We made a drawing showing the earth's outer layer, the **core**.

   We made a drawing showing the earth's center, the core.

2. _____ Some of Earth's **minerals** are rubber, sugar, and wood.

   _____

3. _____ He was having trouble breathing, so they gave him **oxygen**.

   _____

4. _____ A notebook is a good place to **record** important information.

   _____

Name _____ Date _____

Word Pairs

Choose the pair of words from each group that best completes each sentence. Write the words on the lines.

1. Both _____ and _____ are found in the air.

> **carbon**　　　**oxygen**　　　**mineral**　　　**nitrogen**

2. _____ is one type of _____ .

> **mineral**　　　**mantle**　　　**oxygen**　　　**carbon**

3. Both the _____ and the _____ are below the surface of the earth.

> **mantle**　　　**crust**　　　**record**　　　**core**

4. You can use a notebook to _____ the results when you _____ an experiment.

> **mineral**　　　**conduct**　　　**fossil**　　　**record**

Word Study: The Suffix -ation

When the suffix -ation is added to a noun such as *oxygen*, it changes the noun's meaning. The new word means "the process of adding oxygen to something."

> **oxygen** (n.) a colorless mineral in the air that is needed by most life
> **oxygenation** (n.) the process or result of adding oxygen

A. Add the suffix -ation to each element name to make a new word. Use a dictionary to check your spelling and definitions.

Element	+ -ation	Meaning
1. oxygen		
2. nitrogen		
3. carbon		

B. Write a new -ation word on each line.

1. The process of adding carbon dioxide to soda pop is called _____

2. Fish breathe oxygen that plants add to water by _____ .

The Language of Testing

How would you answer a question like this on a test?

What is something that **compares closely to** nitrogen?

- Ⓐ water
- Ⓑ air
- Ⓒ oxygen
- Ⓓ carbon

Tip

Compares closely to means *is most like.*

Test Strategy: If you see a question with the phrase *compares closely to* on a test, rewrite it using the phrase *is most like.*

1. How would you say the above question a different way?

   _____

   _____

Try the strategy again by asking these questions in a different way.

2. What compares closely to *crust*?

   - Ⓐ inner layer
   - Ⓑ center layer
   - Ⓒ outer layer
   - Ⓓ topsoil

   _____

   _____

   _____

   _____

3. Which animal compares most closely to a frog?

   - Ⓐ toad
   - Ⓑ lizard
   - Ⓒ salamander
   - Ⓓ newt

   _____

   _____

   _____

   _____

Name _____ Date _____

On Your Own

Answer the questions.

1. What things are made of **carbon**? _____
_____

2. What things have a **core**? _____
_____

3. What things have a **crust**? _____
_____

4. What animals might you find **fossils** of? _____
_____

5. Why is the earth's **mantle** important? _____
_____

6. Where could you find a **mineral**? _____
_____

7. Where could you find **nitrogen**? _____
_____

8. Why is **oxygen** important? _____
_____

Write On!

You are an explorer who is venturing into "inner" space: you're going to try to find a way to the earth's core! On another sheet of paper, write a journal of your trip and describe your feelings and at least four details of your adventure. Use four or more words from the lesson in your journal.

| mantle | carbon | oxygen | record | mineral |
| core | crust | fossil | conduct | nitrogen |

Vocabulary: Science, SV 9781419034992

Name _____ Date _____

Lesson 7 Assessment

Read the sentences. Look for the best word to complete each sentence. Fill in the circle for the answer you choose. The first one has been done for you.

1. If you were going to the center of the earth, you would be going to its _____.
    - Ⓐ mantle
    - **Ⓑ core**
    - Ⓒ crust
    - Ⓓ nitrogen

2. Salt and iron are _____.
    - Ⓐ fossils
    - Ⓑ carbons
    - Ⓒ minerals
    - Ⓓ records

3. It's important to _____ test results.
    - Ⓐ conduct
    - Ⓑ divide
    - Ⓒ cause
    - Ⓓ record

4. We need _____ to help us breathe.
    - Ⓐ carbon
    - Ⓑ fossils
    - Ⓒ oxygen
    - Ⓓ minerals

5. To find people's opinions you can _____ a survey.
    - Ⓐ record
    - Ⓑ classify
    - Ⓒ notice
    - Ⓓ conduct

6. _____ is found in both the air and the soil.
    - Ⓐ Nitrogen
    - Ⓑ A fossil
    - Ⓒ A mineral
    - Ⓓ The mantle

7. Coal and diamonds are both examples of _____.
    - Ⓐ fossils
    - Ⓑ nitrogen
    - Ⓒ mantles
    - Ⓓ carbon

8. A snail shell can turn into _____.
    - Ⓐ a record
    - Ⓑ nitrogen
    - Ⓒ a fossil
    - Ⓓ oxygen

9. The earth's _____ is made of very hot, oozing rock.
    - Ⓐ mantle
    - Ⓑ carbon
    - Ⓒ crust
    - Ⓓ nitrogen

10. The outer layer of the earth is its _____.
    - Ⓐ core
    - Ⓑ crust
    - Ⓒ mantle
    - Ⓓ mineral

Vocabulary: Science, SV 9781419034992

The Changing Earth

Name _____ Date _____

Read the passage below. Think about the meanings of the new words printed in **bold**. Circle each definition, and draw a line to the word it describes. The first one has been done for you.

Mount St. Helens

Mount St. Helens is in the state of Washington. It isn't just any mountain, however. It is a **volcano**. Volcanoes are mountains that erupt, or explode. In 1980, Mount St. Helens erupted. The explosion actually blew the top off the mountain. It left a large hole called a crater. A large area around the volcano was covered with ash.

Hot **lava**, or melted rock, ash, and gases deep in the earth escape through volcanoes. Sometimes volcanoes erupt because of an **earthquake**. During an earthquake, the outer layer of the earth shifts or moves.

This movement makes the ground shake. It also allows melted rock to come out of the ground.

There are many volcanoes on the North American **continent**. Mount St. Helens was the first volcano to erupt in the main part of the United States since 1917.

Vocabulary Strategy

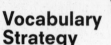

Look for definitions in the text to help you understand the meanings of new words.

✔ New Science Words

continent

noun one of seven large areas of land on Earth

earthquake

noun when the ground shakes because the outer layer of the earth is moving

lava

noun hot, melted rock found deep in the earth

volcano

noun a mountain that sometimes erupts, letting melted rock, ash, and gas come out of the earth

Now read this passage and practice the vocabulary strategy again. Underline any definitions in the passage that help you figure out what the new words in **bold** mean.

The Ice Age

About 12,000 years ago, much of the earth was covered with ice. Giant **glaciers** covered the northern part of the United States. A glacier is a huge, slowly moving sheet of ice. As the glaciers moved, they caused **erosion**. When ice, water, or wind wear away soil or rock, it is called erosion. The erosion shaped the earth's **surface**, or outer layer.

When the glaciers melted, they left behind dirt and rock. This **sediment** was very rich in minerals. That's why the soil in some parts of the country is so good for farming. The glaciers dug out valleys as they moved. Water from the melted glaciers filled the valleys. These became rivers and lakes.

Scientists think that the seas were 300 feet lower during the Ice Age. That's as deep as a football field is long! This is because so much water was frozen in the glaciers. Ice Age glaciers were thousands of miles wide and over a mile thick. That's a lot of ice!

More New Science Words

erosion

noun   the wearing away of dirt or rock by wind, ice, or water

glacier

noun   a huge, slowly moving sheet of ice

sediment

noun   sand and dirt at the bottom of a river or lake, or that is left behind by moving water

surface

noun   the top or outside layer of something

Use the Strategy

Look at a chapter in your textbook that your teacher identifies. Use definitions in the text to help you figure out the meaning of any new words you find.

Other Useful Words

effect

noun   a change that results from some action

recognize

verb   to know what something is because of its features

Name _____ Date _____

Matching

Finish the sentences in Group A with words from Group B. Write the letter of the word on the line.

Group A

1. Deep grooves formed on the hillside where moving water had caused _____.

2. The top layer or _____ of the earth has valleys, mountains, and hills.

3. The movement caused by the _____ hurt several buildings.

4. One icy _____ in Alaska is almost 50 miles wide.

Group B

A. earthquake
B. erosion
C. glacier
D. surface

Group A

5. Hot _____ flowed down the side of the mountain.

6. The delicious smell of baking pies had the _____ of making me hungry.

7. The _____ in the river came from soil that was washed in by the rain.

8. I didn't _____ him because he was wearing a mask.

Group B

E. effect
F. recognize
G. sediment
H. lava

Lesson 8: The Changing Earth
Vocabulary: Science, SV 9781419034992

Name _____ Date _____

Word Challenge: Finish the Idea

Read the incomplete sentences below. Write an ending for each. The first one has been done for you.

1. We knew we were in an **earthquake** because _the ground was moving up_

   and down.

2. The United States is not a **continent** because _____

   _____

3. We knew that the mountain was a **volcano** because _____

   _____

4. Mom didn't **recognize** me because _____

   _____

Word Challenge: What's Your Answer?

Read each question and write an answer on the line. Answer the questions in complete sentences. The first one has been done for you.

1. What in your town is an example of **erosion**? _The deep grooves in_

   the side of the hill are an example of erosion.

2. What might be the **effect** of eating twenty candy bars? _____

   _____

3. Where would you find **sediment**? _____

   _____

4. Describe the **surface** of your desk. _____

   _____

Name _____ Date _____

Word Pairs

Choose the pair of words from each group that best completes each sentence. Write the words on the lines.

1. There was _____ in the water from all the _____.

   continent   **erosion**   **effects**   **sediment**

2. Part of the _____ was covered by a _____ during the Ice Age.

   continent   **earthquake**   **glacier**   **volcano**

3. During the _____, the _____ of the earth moved.

   earthquake   **lava**   **volcano**   **surface**

4. Scientists could tell the mountain was a _____ even though there was no _____.

   erosion   **earthquake**   **lava**   **volcano**

Word Study: The Suffixes -ology and -ologist

When suffixes -ology and -ologist are added to nouns such as glacier, they change the noun's meaning.
- -ology means "the study of": glaciology
- -ologist means "a person who studies": glaciologist

glacier (n.) a huge, slowly moving sheet of ice
glaciology (n.) the study of glaciers
glaciologist (n.) a person who studies glaciers

A. Add -ology and -ologist to the words below. You may use a dictionary to check your spelling.

	+ -ology	+ -ologist
1. sediment		
2. volcano		

B. Write a sentence for one of the -ology words and one of the -ologist words you made. Make sure your sentences show that you understand what each word means.

1. _____

2. _____

Vocabulary: Science, SV 9781419034992

Name _____ Date _____

The Language of Testing

How would you answer a question like this on a test?

What was a **major effect** of the flooding?

Ⓐ New levees were built.
Ⓑ Most of the crops were lost.
Ⓒ Erosion made the bridge collapse.
Ⓓ All of the above

Tip

Major effect means something very important happened because of or as a result of something else.

Test Strategy: If you see a question that uses the phrase *major effect*, notice what comes after it. It is usually an important event. What happened because of this thing or event? Read each answer, and add to it *because of the* (event). You can use this to test which answers are right or wrong.

1. What phrase would you use to test each answer choice above?

_____

_____

Try the strategy again by adding a test phrase to the answer choices below. Write your test phrase below each question.

2. What was a major effect of the Ice Age?

Ⓐ The sea level rose.
Ⓑ Melting ice caused earthquakes.
Ⓒ Glaciers changed Earth's surface.
Ⓓ People migrated from Asia.

_____

_____

_____

3. What is a major effect of water freezing and melting?

Ⓐ Rock cracks or breaks apart.
Ⓑ Beaches are washed away.
Ⓒ Erosion removes the topsoil.
Ⓓ Waterways become clogged.

_____

_____

_____

Vocabulary: Science, SV 9781419034992

Name _____ Date _____

Answer the questions.

1. Name all of the **continents**. _____

_____

2. What are some of the effects of an **earthquake**? _____

_____

3. How can you stop **erosion**? _____

_____

4. Where could you find a **glacier**? _____

_____

5. What might **lava** do to things it flows over? _____

_____

6. Where would you find **sediment**? _____

_____

7. What does the **surface** of an orange look like? _____

_____

8. What comes out of a **volcano** when it explodes? _____

_____

Write On!

You're a reporter for the local newspaper, and you've witnessed a major earthquake or volcanic eruption. On another sheet of paper, write a newspaper article that describes at least four details of the event. Use four or more words from the lesson correctly.

lava	earthquake	glacier	continent	volcano
recognize	erosion	surface	sediment	effect

Name _____ Date _____

Lesson 8 Assessment

Read the sentences. Look for the best word to complete each sentence. Fill in the circle for the answer you choose. The first one has been done for you.

1. A _____ is a very large area of land.
   - (A) volcano
   - (B) glacier
   - (C) continent
   - (D) lava

2. Water and wind can cause _____.
   - (A) erasure
   - (B) erosion
   - (C) an earthquake
   - (D) lava

3. If you know what something looks like, you will probably be able to _____ it.
   - (A) effect
   - (B) erode
   - (C) recognize
   - (D) adapt

4. Many years ago, _____ carved out valleys.
   - (A) earthquakes
   - (B) volcanoes
   - (C) lava
   - (D) glaciers

5. Lakes, mountains, and rivers are all part of the earth's _____.
   - (A) erosions
   - (B) sediment
   - (C) surface
   - (D) effects

6. A major earthquake will have many _____ on the population.
   - (A) sediments
   - (B) effects
   - (C) erosions
   - (D) surfaces

7. _____ sometimes let gas out of the earth.
   - (A) Erosions
   - (B) Glaciers
   - (C) Sediments
   - (D) Volcanoes

8. _____ can settle at the bottom of a river.
   - (A) Volcanoes
   - (B) Glaciers
   - (C) Sediment
   - (D) Continents

9. _____ can cause a volcano to erupt.
   - (A) Glaciers
   - (B) Earthquakes
   - (C) Sediment
   - (D) Erosion

10. _____ is melted rock.
    - (A) Sediment
    - (B) Erosion
    - (C) Lava
    - (D) A volcano

Lesson 9

Name _____ Date _____

Space

Read the passage below. Think about the meanings of the new words printed in **bold**. Create connections between the new words and words you know. These will help you remember what the new words mean. Write these connections near the new words in the passage. The first one has been done for you.

Calendars

the sun

In the past, calendars were based on the sun and the moon. **Solar** calendars followed the sun's path in the sky. People noticed that sometimes the sun was higher in the sky. Sometimes it was lower. From this, they figured out the number of days in a year. Today we know that the earth spins around an imaginary line or **axis**. The axis is tilted. So the sun appears in different places in the sky during different seasons.

Lunar calendars were based on the **phases** of the moon. For example, a full moon and new moon are two of the phases. In these calendars, a month was about 29 days long.

In the calendar we use today, each year has 12 months and 365 days. But don't forget leap year, which has 366 days!

Vocabulary Strategy

Create connections between new words and words you know. You can use a Word Anchor chart to help you create connections.

New Science Words

axis

noun an imaginary line that runs through the center of something

lunar

adjective having to do with the moon

phase

noun a stage in the way the moon looks from Earth

solar

adjective having to do with the sun

Name _____ Date _____

Now read this passage and practice the vocabulary strategies again. Write near the new words any connections you can use to "anchor" the meaning of the new words.

 # Galileo

Galileo was an Italian scientist. He lived in the late 1500s and early 1600s. He built the first telescope, a tool that a scientist can use to look closely at the sky. Using his telescope, Galileo figured out that Earth moves in an **orbit** around the sun. An orbit is like a curved path or circle.

Galileo also discovered that the earth **revolves**, or spins around. He also saw that **planets**, like Earth, had **satellites**. An example of a satellite is a moon that orbits around a planet. He saw four of the moons that orbit the planet Jupiter through his telescope.

Today, people who study the planets and stars use a telescope like Galileo's. They also have tools that help them **measure** things in space. Without Galileo's ideas, scientists today would find it pretty hard to **explore**, or learn about the sky.

"Are you sure this is the best way to **measure** a **planet**?"

 ## More New Science Words

orbit
noun the curved path an object makes around a larger object
verb to travel in a curved path around something

planet
noun a large rock, such as Earth, that moves around a star

revolve
verb to spin in a circle around a center

satellite
noun an object that moves around a larger object in space

 ## Other Useful Words

explore
verb to learn about something, or to travel through an unknown area to learn about it

measure
verb to figure out the size of an object or how far two places are from each other

 ## Use the Strategy

Look at a chapter in your textbook that your teacher identifies. Use associations to help you anchor the meanings of any new words you find.

    Vocabulary: Science, SV 9781419034992

Name _____ Date _____

Finish the Paragraph

Use the words in **bold** to finish the paragraph below. Write the correct word in the blank. One word will not be used.

exploring	**axis**	**lunar**	**orbits**	**planets**
revolve	**satellite**	**solar**	**measure**	**phases**

Our class is _____ space. Since we could not travel there, we
                  1

built a model. We have eight _____ and each one moves around, or
                                2

_____, the sun. We have a moon, or _____,
  3   **4**

that orbits Earth. Our model of Earth can actually spin on its _____!
                                                            5

Last week, we took the model to another class. We told them that our model

was called the _____ system. It is called this because all of
                        6

the planets orbit the sun. The teacher told us that the root word for *solar* is *sol*,

which means *sun*. She also said that *luna* means *moon*. So *luna* is the root word

for _____. The moon goes through many stages, or
             7

_____, each month. Next week, we want to learn how scientists
             8

_____ the distance between stars. I hope I have a big enough ruler!
             9

Name _____ Date _____

Word Challenge: Finish the Idea

Read the incomplete sentences below. Write an ending for each. The first one has been done for you.

1. Mars is my favorite **planet** because _it is red and very hot._

2. I would love to **explore** Jupiter because _____

_____

3. I would not like living on a **satellite** because _____

_____

4. Some people use **solar** energy because _____

_____

Word Challenge: True or False

Write **T** next to each sentence that is true. Write **F** next to each sentence that is false. Rewrite the false sentences. The first one has been done for you.

1. __T__ The earth **revolves** once every 24 hours.

2. _____ A normal **orbit** is a straight line.

_____

3. _____ During each **phase**, the moon looks the same.

_____

4. _____ If something is **lunar**, it has to do with the moon.

_____

Vocabulary: Science, SV 9781419034992

Name _____ Date _____

Word Connections

In the spaces at the top of the wheel, write the words from the box that connect to the center word or idea. In the spaces at the bottom of the wheel, write the words that do not connect.

axis	lunar	orbit	planet	satellite	solar

YES

moon

X   X

X

NO

Word Study: The Prefix *non-*

When the prefix *non-* is added to an adjective such as *lunar,* it changes the adjective's meaning. The new word now means the opposite of the old word. *Non-* can mean *not* or *without.*

lunar (adj.) having to do with the moon
nonlunar (adj.) having nothing to do with the moon

A. Add the prefix *non-* to each word to make a new word. Write your own definition for each. Use a dictionary to check your spelling and your definitions.

	+ *non-*	Meaning
1. **solar**		
2. **example**		
3. **sense**		

B. Write your own sentences using two words from the chart.

1. _____

2. _____

Vocabulary: Science, SV 9781419034992

Name _____   Date _____

The Language of Testing

How would you answer a question like this on a test?

The Planets

Name	Diameter	Distance from Sun
Mercury	3,032 miles	36 million miles
Venus	7,519 miles	67 million miles
Earth	7,926 miles	93 million miles

Based on the table, which of these planets is the smallest?

Ⓐ Earth   Ⓒ Mercury

Ⓑ Venus

Tip

When you see the words *based on* in a question, it means you need to look at a map, chart, or picture to answer the question.

Test Strategy: Circle or underline words or phrases in the question that tell you what to do. In the question above you would circle or underline *based on the table*. You can also rewrite the question to tell you to *look at the table to find the information you need.*

1. How could you say the question above in a different way?

_____

_____

Try the strategy again by asking these questions in a different way.

2. Based on the table, which of these planets is closest to the sun?

Ⓐ Mercury

Ⓑ Venus

Ⓒ Earth

3. Based on the table, which two of these planets are about the same size?

Ⓐ Mercury and Venus

Ⓑ Venus and Earth

Ⓒ Mercury and Earth

Name _____ Date _____

 On Your Own

Answer the questions.

1. What things need an **axis**? _____

_____

2. What things can the word **lunar** describe? _____

_____

3. What other things **orbit** the sun? _____

_____

4. How can you measure a **phase**? _____

_____

5. What **planets** are close to Earth? _____

_____

6. How can you make something **revolve**? _____

_____

7. Where could you find a **satellite**? _____

_____

8. Where does **solar** power come from? _____

_____

Write On!

You're a scientist who has just made some important discoveries. You want to share these with a friend. On another sheet of paper, write a letter to your friend and describe at least four of your discoveries. Use four or more words from the lesson correctly.

axis	solar	lunar	orbit	satellite
phase	measure	planet	explore	revolve

Name _____ Date _____

Lesson 9 Assessment

Read the sentences. Look for the best word to complete each sentence. Fill in the circle for the answer you choose. The first one has been done for you.

1. _____ move around planets.
   - (A) Orbits
   - (B) Phases
   - (C) Planets
   - (D) Satellites

2. Everything related to the moon is _____.
   - (A) solar
   - (B) lunar
   - (C) an orbit
   - (D) an axis

3. Earth completes one _____ around the sun every 365 days.
   - (A) revolve
   - (B) planet
   - (C) orbit
   - (D) phase

4. Mars and Mercury are _____.
   - (A) measures
   - (B) phases
   - (C) orbits
   - (D) planets

5. Some old calendars were based on the _____ of the moon.
   - (A) phases
   - (B) orbits
   - (C) axis
   - (D) satellites

6. The sun is at the center of our _____ system.
   - (A) satellite
   - (B) solar
   - (C) lunar
   - (D) orbit

7. Astronomers _____ temperatures and other conditions in outer space.
   - (A) orbit
   - (B) revolve
   - (C) measure
   - (D) axis

8. The earth's _____ is an imaginary line.
   - (A) satellite
   - (B) phase
   - (C) planet
   - (D) axis

9. The moon spins on its _____ .
   - (A) phases
   - (B) revolves
   - (C) axis
   - (D) satellite

10. The United States space program has sent special probes to _____ Mars.
    - (A) explore
    - (B) phase
    - (C) orbit
    - (D) revolve around

Weather

Read the passage below. Think about the meanings of the new words printed in **bold**. Circle any synonyms, or words that might mean the same as the new words. Draw an arrow from each synonym to the new word it describes. The first one has been done for you.

TV Weather

<table>
<tr><td>

Vocabulary Strategy

Use synonyms, or words that mean about the same as the new words, to help you understand their meaning. Look for clues like *or* to help you find synonyms in a text.

</td><td>

When you watch the weather on TV, you often see a weather person pointing to a map. This map is covered with symbols. For example, a **front**, or edge of a mass of cold or warm air, is shown by a line and arrows. A large *L* on the map means that there is a low **pressure** system nearby. In a low pressure system, the air isn't pressing down strongly. Sometimes, a drawing of a large **thermometer** pops up. The large thermometer tells the **temperature**, or how hot or cold it is outside.

</td><td>

During the show, the weather person sees only a green wall. A computer adds the maps, symbols, and **labels** later. So how do weather people know what to point to? They watch another television that you can't see! Next time you watch the weather on TV, try to catch the weather person watching TV, too!

</td></tr>
</table>

New Science Words

front
noun the edge of a mass of warm or cold air

pressure
noun the effect of one thing pushing on another

temperature
noun the amount of warmth in something

thermometer
noun a tool for measuring how warm something is

Name _____ Date _____

Now read this passage and practice the vocabulary strategy again. Circle any synonyms and draw an arrow from each to the word it describes.

Water, Water, Everywhere

Water is always changing. One major change is when water turns into air. This is called **evaporation**. Water in rivers, lakes, oceans, and even in the ground evaporates into the **atmosphere**. The atmosphere is the mass of air around Earth. In the atmosphere, wetness, or **humidity**, makes clouds. When the clouds touch cooler air, the water becomes rain or snow. The water falls back to Earth and the changes begin again.

There are some places that have a dry **climate**. In a dry climate, water in the air doesn't come back down as rain or snow. The water in these areas still evaporates, however. Can you **predict** or guess where it goes? It goes up into the atmosphere and falls down again as rain or snow somewhere else. It's all part of the cycle.

"Drink the water quickly, before it **evaporates**!"

More New Science Words

atmosphere
  noun   the layer of air around the earth

climate
  noun   the usual weather of a large area

evaporation
  noun   the way in which water seems to disappear into the air

humidity
  noun   the amount of wetness in the air

Use the Strategy

Look at a chapter in your textbook that your teacher identifies. Use synonyms in the text to help you figure out the meaning of any new words you find. Keep track of the new words and synonyms in a chart.

Other Useful Words

label
  verb   to place a name on something

predict
  verb   to say what will happen

Vocabulary: Science, SV 9781419034992

Name _____ Date _____

 The Right Word

Read each sentence. Look at the word or phrase that is underlined. Write one of the words from the box that means the same or almost the same thing as the underlined part of the sentence.

thermometer	humidity	front	pressure

1. _____ The wetness in the air made it feel warmer than it was.

2. _____ The tool that shows how warm it is read 98.6°.

3. _____ The edge of a mass of cold air moved down from Canada.

4. _____ I couldn't keep the door closed because the pushing of the wind was too strong.

temperature	label	predict	climate

5. _____ The usual weather in a desert is hot and dry.

6. _____ We had to name the parts of the frog.

7. _____ The amount of hot or cold dropped to freezing last night.

8. _____ How are scientists able to guess when big storms are going to happen?

Name _____ Date _____

Word Challenge: Would You Rather . . .

Read the questions below. Think of a response and write it on the line. Write your responses in complete sentences. The first one has been done for you.

1. Would you rather feel high **humidity** or low humidity? Why? _I'd rather feel_

high humidity because places with low humidity are too dry.

2. Would you rather **predict** the weather or the future? Why? _____

_____

3. Would you rather live in a freezing cold or a boiling hot **climate**? Why? _____

_____

4. Would you rather have a warm **front** or a cold front move through your area? Why?

_____

_____

Word Challenge: Word Relationships

Read the groups of words below. Write the word from the lesson that best goes with each group. The first one has been done for you.

1. ____thermometer____ measure, numbers, temperature

2. _____ weight, push

3. _____ water, dry, disappear

4. _____ warmth, fever, thermometer

Lesson 10: Weather
Vocabulary: Science, SV 9781419034992

Extend the Meaning

Write the letter of the word or phrase that best completes each sentence.

1. Another word for **atmosphere** would be _____.
   a lunar
   b. ecosystem
   c. air

2. If it was hot and **humid** you might _____.
   a. feel sleepy
   b. feel sweaty
   c. increase your exercise

3. When a **front** passes through, _____.
   a. the weather stays the same
   b. it usually starts to rain
   c. the weather usually changes

4. You would feel **pressure** if _____.
   a. someone squeezed your arm
   b. you got a flat tire on your bike
   c. it started to rain very hard

Word Study: The -ed Ending

The -ed ending is added to a root verb when talking about what happened in the past. If the verb ends in
- -e, just add -d: evaporated.
- a consonant, add -ed: turned.

> **evaporate** (v.) to make water go into the air
> **evaporated** (v., past tense) to have made water go into the air

A. Add -ed to the words below. Write a definition for each new word. You may use a dictionary to check your spelling and definitions.

	+ -ed	Meaning
1. **label**		
2. **predict**		
3. **pressure**		

B. Complete the story with -ed words from the chart.

Carlos reads weather reports for a TV news show. Here is the report that he read

on Thursday night: "I was right when I _____ rain for Wednesday

night. It rained all night! I predict more rain for Friday. It will fall north of our city. I

have _____ those areas on the map. Good night, everyone."

Name _____   Date _____

The Language of Testing

How would you answer a question like this on a test?

Which of the following terms is **associated with** weather?

- Ⓐ evaporation
- Ⓑ thermometer
- Ⓒ earthquake
- Ⓓ carbon

Test Strategy: If you see a question that contains the phrase *associated with*, rewrite it using the phrases *related to* or *connected to*.

1. How could you say the question above in a different way?

   _____

   _____

Try the strategy again by asking these questions in a different way.

2. Which is associated with the atmosphere?

   - Ⓐ air
   - Ⓑ temperature
   - Ⓒ sunlight
   - Ⓓ phases of the moon

   _____

   _____

   _____

   _____

3. What is associated with the movement of weather patterns?

   - Ⓐ humidity
   - Ⓑ evaporation
   - Ⓒ the water cycle
   - Ⓓ front

   _____

   _____

   _____

   _____

Name _____ Date _____

Answer the questions.

1. Why do we need an **atmosphere**? _____

_____

2. Describe the **climate** of your state. _____

_____

3. What are the signs of **evaporation**? _____

_____

4. How do you know when there is a **front** coming? _____

_____

5. How can you tell if the **humidity** is high or low today? ___

_____

6. Which of your senses measures **pressure**? _____

_____

7. How can you measure **temperature**? _____

_____

8. How does a **thermometer** work? _____

_____

Write On!

You are the new weather forecaster for your local TV station. On another sheet of paper, write your prediction for tomorrow's weather. Use four or more words from the lesson correctly.

front	**label**	**pressure**	**temperature**	**thermometer**
predict	**atmosphere**	**humidity**	**climate**	**evaporation**

Name _____   Date _____

Lesson 10 Assessment

Read the sentences. Look for the best word to complete each sentence. Fill in the circle for the answer you choose. The first one has been done for you.

1. A _____ is a tool you need when you deal with the weather.
   - (A) temperature
   - (B) thermometer
   - (C) front
   - (D) label

2. You might find temperatures, fronts, and pressure _____ on a weather map.
   - (A) evaporated
   - (B) labeled
   - (C) predicted
   - (D) measured

3. If temperatures start to fall tomorrow, would you expect a warm or a cold _____ to be moving into the area?
   - (A) front
   - (B) pressure
   - (C) thermometer
   - (D) atmosphere

4. _____ is how water "disappears" into the air.
   - (A) Pressure
   - (B) A front
   - (C) Evaporation
   - (D) Humidity

5. If a team has good players, you can _____ that they probably will win.
   - (A) label
   - (B) compare
   - (C) measure
   - (D) predict

6. The amount of wetness in the air is the _____.
   - (A) evaporation
   - (B) humidity
   - (C) atmosphere
   - (D) temperature

7. The words *tropical*, *temperate*, and *desert* all describe _____.
   - (A) climates
   - (B) temperatures
   - (C) evaporations
   - (D) atmospheres

8. The water from rivers and lakes becomes part of the _____.
   - (A) front
   - (B) atmosphere
   - (C) temperature
   - (D) climate

9. If someone steps on your foot, you can feel the _____ inside your shoe.
   - (A) front
   - (B) temperature
   - (C) pressure
   - (D) humidity

10. _____ are often cooler at night.
    - (A) Evaporations
    - (B) Fronts
    - (C) Temperatures
    - (D) Pressure

The Earth's Resources

Read the passage below. Think about the meaning of the words printed in **bold**. Circle any words that begin with *en-* or *ex-*. Write what you think each word means near it. Remember that the prefix *en-* means "in," and *ex-* means "out." The first one has been done for you.

Copper Country

Vocabulary Strategy

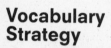

Use prefixes and suffixes you know to help you understand the meanings of new words.

A certain part of Michigan is called copper country. That is because there are so many **deposits**, or natural layers, of copper there. Long ago, Native Americans discovered the copper. Much of it was on the earth's surface.

take out

Around 1840, people began to dig deep mines to (**extract**) the copper from the ground. Thousands of people came to Michigan hoping to make a lot of money with the copper.

The mines caused a lot of **pollution** that dirtied the soil and the

water. The owners of the mines also did nothing to **enrich** the land after taking so much out of it. As the copper ran out, most people moved away. Today, old mine shafts and ghost towns dot the landscape in what was once copper country.

New Science Words

deposit

noun   natural layers of something that build up over time

enrich

verb   to make something better by adding other things

extract

verb   to take something out of something else

pollution

noun   something that dirties and harms the water, soil, and air

Name _____ Date _____

Now read this passage and underline any words that begin with *re-* or end in *-able*. Write what you think each underlined word means next to it. Remember that *re-* means "to do again," and that *-able* tells you what something can do or have done to it.

The Three *R*'s of the Environment

Have you ever heard of the three *R*'s of the environment? They are **reduce**, reuse, and **recycle**. Many people believe that you can help reduce pollution if you follow the three *R*'s. But just what do they mean?

The first *R*, *reduce*, means that you should use less of everything. You should buy things with less packaging. You should use less water. You should also use less gas and electricity.

The second *R*, *reuse*, means that you shouldn't just use something once and throw it away. Having **reusable** things means you use a lunch box over and over again. It means you take your grocery bags back to the market. It means washing a plastic spoon instead of throwing it out.

The third *R*, *recycle*, means that you don't put anything in the trash that can be recycled. You can recycle glass, paper, and many plastic items. This way we **conserve** our natural resources.

Jacob couldn't see that he was part of the problem.

 More New Science Words

conserve
   verb   to use something carefully so it will last longer

recycle
   verb   to use something over again, sometimes in a different way

reduce
   verb   to make the amount of something less or smaller

reusable
   adjective   can be used more than one time

Use the Strategy

Look at a chapter in your textbook that your teacher identifies. Use prefixes and suffixes you know to help you figure out the meaning of any new words you find.

 Other Useful Words

communicate
   verb   to share information through speaking, writing, or movements

purpose
   noun   the reason for doing something

Name _____ Date _____

Extend the Meaning

Write the letter of the word or phrase that best completes each sentence.

1. When we _____ something, we're careful how much we use.

   a. conserve

   b. extract

   c. reduce

2. We tried to _____ the amount of gasoline we use.

   a. enrich

   b. reduce

   c. recycle

3. Dogs _____ by barking and wagging their tails.

   a. recycle

   b. conserve

   c. communicate

4. Miners _____ minerals such as copper, coal, and gold from the earth.

   a. enrich

   b. extract

   c. recycle

5. The _____, or reason, for turning off the lights is to save energy.

   a. pollution

   b. purpose

   c. deposit

6. The _____ was so bad that the air looked brown.

   a. pollution

   b. deposit

   c. reduce

7. In 1849, large _____ of gold were found in California.

   a. pollution

   b. deposits

   c. extract

8. They used plant food to _____ the soil.

   a. reduce

   b. extract

   c. enrich

Name _____ Date _____

Word Challenge: Example/Not an Example

Think of things that are and are not examples of the words listed below. Write your responses in the chart. The first one has been done for you.

	Example	**Not an Example**
1. **deposit**	You are digging in your yard and you find gold.	You are digging in your yard and you find a tree root.
2. **reduce**		
3. **communicate**		
4. **conserve**		

Word Challenge: What's Your Reason?

Read the statements below. Think of a reason for each statement and write it on the line. Write your reasons in complete sentences. The first one has been done for you.

1. It is important to **recycle**. When we recycle, we use fewer natural resources.

2. We should stop **pollution**. _____

_____

3. Fast-food restaurants should use **reusable** containers. _____

_____

4. Farmers should **enrich** the soil. _____

_____

Name _____ Date _____

What's the Answer?

Circle the letter of each correct answer. Some questions may have more than one correct answer.

1. What are some effects of **pollution**?
a. poor air quality
b. dirty water
c. fresh air
d. snow and rain

2. What is an example of a **deposit**?
a. a large field
b. an area with iron ore
c. a group of lakes
d. a nesting area for birds

3. How can people **conserve** resources?
a. use less gasoline
b. use more water
c. recycle
d. use more reusable containers

4. How can people **enrich** the earth?
a. mine it for minerals
b. put nutrients back into the soil
c. cut down trees
d. conserve fuel

Word Study: The Suffixes -er and -or

When the suffix -er or -or is added to a word such as *deposit,* it changes its meaning. The new word names a person or thing that does a job or action.

deposit (v.) to put something somewhere, or to leave something behind
depositor (n.) a person or animal that puts something somewhere or leaves something behind

Add the -er or -or suffix to make new words. Write a definition for each new word. Use a dictionary to check your spelling and your definitions.

	+ -er or -or	Meaning
1. extract		
2. pollute		
3. recycle		
4. communicate		

Vocabulary: Science, SV 9781419034992

Name _____   Date _____

How would you answer a question like this on a test?

What does **the diagram illustrate**?

(A) a mine

(B) erosion

(C) the inside of a building

(D) how to build a machine

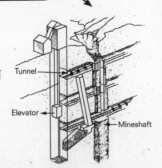

Tunnel

Elevator

Mineshaft

Tip

When a question asks you what something *illustrates*, you need to look at a picture to find the answer to the question.

Test Strategy: If you see a question that asks you what something *illustrates*, rewrite it to ask what the diagram, chart, table, or graph shows.

1. How could you say the question above in a different way?

_____

_____

Try the strategy again by asking these questions in a different way.

2. What is illustrated by the diagram?

(A) a frog

(B) a frog's internal organs

(C) a tadpole

(D) a toad

_____

_____

_____

_____

3. Which diagram illustrates how aluminum is recycled?

(A) 1   (C) 3

(B) 2   (D) 4

_____

_____

_____

_____

www.harcourtschoolsupply.com
91
Lesson 11: The Earth's Resources
Vocabulary: Science, SV 9781419034992

Name _____ Date _____

Answer the questions.

1. What things should you **conserve**? _____

_____

2. What things leave behind a **deposit**? _____

_____

3. How do you **enrich** something? _____

_____

4. What can you **extract** from the earth? _____

_____

5. What are some kinds of **pollution**? _____

_____

6. What things can you **recycle**? _____

_____

7. How can you **reduce** the amount of water you use every day? _____

_____

8. Name some things that are **reusable**. _____

_____

Write On!

You are in charge of your community's three *R*'s of the environment—*reduce, reuse,* and *recycle*. On another sheet of paper, write a letter giving at least three reasons why people in your community should practice the three *R*'s. Use four or more words from the lesson correctly.

extract	**pollution**	**conserve**	**recycle**	**reusable**
reduce	**deposit**	**purpose**	**communicate**	**enrich**

Name _____ Date _____

Lesson 11 Assessment

Read the sentences. Look for the best word to complete each sentence. Fill in the circle for the answer you choose. The first one has been done for you.

1. To help fight _____, some cities do not allow cars in certain areas.
   - Ⓐ deposits
   - Ⓑ purposes
   - Ⓒ recycling
   - Ⓓ pollution

2. We should try to _____ the amount of electricity we use.
   - Ⓐ recycle
   - Ⓑ reduce
   - Ⓒ enrich
   - Ⓓ extract

3. The opposite of consume is _____.
   - Ⓐ conserve
   - Ⓑ communicate
   - Ⓒ reduce
   - Ⓓ extract

4. If you can use something over and over, it is _____.
   - Ⓐ enrichable
   - Ⓑ extractable
   - Ⓒ reusable
   - Ⓓ reducable

5. People _____ information and ideas with others.
   - Ⓐ conserve
   - Ⓑ reduce
   - Ⓒ communicate
   - Ⓓ extract

6. Newspapers, cans, and bottles can all be _____.
   - Ⓐ extracted
   - Ⓑ recycled
   - Ⓒ communicated
   - Ⓓ enriched

7. Gold and silver can be _____ from the ground.
   - Ⓐ recycled
   - Ⓑ reused
   - Ⓒ conserved
   - Ⓓ extracted

8. To grow healthy crops, farmers need to _____ the soil.
   - Ⓐ extract
   - Ⓑ erosion
   - Ⓒ enrich
   - Ⓓ reduce

9. _____ are natural layers that build up over time.
   - Ⓐ Purposes
   - Ⓑ Deposits
   - Ⓒ Nutrients
   - Ⓓ Erosions

10. Mary's _____ in life was to become an astronaut.
    - Ⓐ pollution
    - Ⓑ communication
    - Ⓒ purpose
    - Ⓓ method

Name _____ Date _____

Matter

Read the passage below. Think about the meanings of the new words printed in **bold**. Underline any words and phrases that contrast a word you know with a new word or idea. The first one has been done for you.

 ## A Tiny Atom

Matter, or everything that you can see or touch, is made of tiny pieces. These bits are called **atoms**. You can think of atoms like grains of sand that make up a beach. A grain of sand, however, is also matter and can be broken into smaller parts. <u>Unlike a grain of sand, an atom is the smallest piece that matter can be broken into.</u> A human hair, for example, is over a million atoms wide! Yet atoms are made up of parts that are even smaller.

Tiny things called protons and neutrons make up most of an atom's **mass**. Mass is how much matter something has inside of it. Protons and neutrons are the center, or nucleus, of the atom. The nucleus of the atom has **density**. It is heavy for being so small. If an atom were about two miles wide, the nucleus would be about the size of a ping-pong ball. Unlike the nucleus of the atom, however, the outer part of the atom has little density. More tiny things called electrons whirl around in this space.

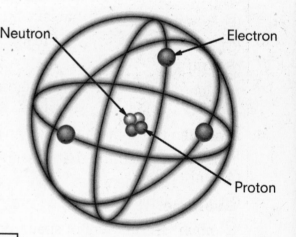

Neutron · Electron · Proton

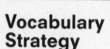

Vocabulary Strategy

Use contrasts to help you understand the meanings of new words. Look for clues that point out contrasts, such as *unlike*, *instead*, or *different from*.

✔ New Science Words

atom
 noun the smallest part of an element

density
 noun how thick something is, or how much it weighs compared to its size

mass
 noun how much matter something has inside it

matter
 noun anything that takes up space and has weight

Name _____ Date _____

Now read this passage and practice the vocabulary strategy again. Underline any words and phrases that contrast something you know with a new word or idea. Look for clues like *unlike*, *instead*, or *different from*.

Drink It, Breathe It, Walk on It

All matter comes in three states or forms. Those three states are **solid**, **liquid**, and **gas**. The atoms in a solid, like a rock, are usually closer together than the atoms of a liquid or a gas. Unlike the atoms in a solid, the atoms in a liquid like water are farther apart. The atoms in a gas, like oxygen, are even farther apart.

Each state of matter also has **volume**. In other words, it takes up space. Usually the solid state of matter has the least volume. In **general**, a liquid has greater volume. One specific liquid, water, is a little different, though. Instead of growing smaller when it freezes into ice, its solid form, it expands, or grows. That's why ice floats in a glass of water. Unlike both a solid and a liquid, a gas can expand to fill any size space. Its atoms have no certain **order** in their movements, so a gas has no shape. That's why there are so many gases in the air we breathe.

More New Science Words

gas
noun   something that is neither a liquid nor a solid, such as steam

liquid
noun   something that is neither a gas nor a solid, such as milk

solid
noun   something that is neither a gas nor a liquid, such as a penny

volume
noun   the amount of space an object takes up or can hold, or how loud or soft a sound is

Wow! Milk is **liquid** ice cream!

No, **solid** milk is ice cream!

Use the Strategy

Look at a chapter in your textbook that your teacher identifies. Use contrasts in the text to help you figure out the meaning of any new words you find. Keep track of these in a chart.

Other Useful Words

general
adjective   not specific

order
noun   the way things are placed
verb   to place things in a certain way

Vocabulary: Science, SV 9781419034992

Name _____ Date _____

Finish the Sentence

Choose a word to finish each sentence. Write the correct word on the line.

1. The water we drink is a _____.

   gas   **solid**   **liquid**   **ice**

2. All _____ in the universe has weight.

   volume   **density**   **matter**   **atom**

3. Something in its _____ state has a shape.

   solid   **gas**   **liquid**   **atomic**

4. A gas will grow to fill the _____ of any space.

   atom   **matter**   **volume**   **solid**

5. A _____ weighs less than a liquid.

   atom   **gas**   **solid**   **volume**

6. An _____ is very small.

   mass   **volume**   **solid**   **atom**

7. The teacher had us line up in _____ from

   shortest to tallest.

   order   **atom**   **volume**   **solid**

8. A _____ store sells a lot of different things.

   mass   **liquid**   **general**   **volume**

Vocabulary: Science, SV 9781419034992

Name _____ Date _____

Word Challenge: Which Word?

Think of a statement for each word below that gives a strong clue about its meaning. Write your statement next to the word. The first one has been done for you.

1. **atom** _"I am the smallest part of something."_____

2. **solid** _____

3. **volume** _____

4. **gas** _____

Word Challenge: Correct or Incorrect

Read the sentences below. Decide if the new words in the lesson are used correctly or incorrectly. Write **C** if the sentence is correct. Write **I** if the sentence is incorrect. Rewrite the incorrect sentences. The first one has been done for you.

1. __I__ There are eight states of **matter**.

   _There are three states of matter._____

2. _____ The **mass** of an object measures how much space it fills.

   _____

3. _____ The ocean is filled with a salty **liquid**.

   _____

4. _____ Her interests are so **general** that she has very few hobbies.

   _____

Name _____ Date _____

Analogies

Use a word from the box to finish each sentence. Write the word on the line.

solid	liquid	atom	general

1. Lava is to liquid as rock is to _____.

2. Beach is to a grain of sand as matter is to _____.

3. Orderly is to messy as specific is to _____.

4. Air is to gas as milk is to _____.

Word Study: The Suffix -ify

When the suffix -ify is added to a noun such as gas, it does two things:
- First, it makes the noun a verb: gasify.
- Second, it changes the word's meaning. The word now means "to turn something into gas."

> **Liquid** is a little different. Drop the -id from the end of liquid before adding -efy.
>
> **liquid** (n.) something that is neither a gas nor a solid, such as milk
>
> **liquefy** (v.) to turn something into liquid

A. Add the -ify or -efy suffix to make a new word.

	+ -ify
1. **solid**	
2. **liquid**	
3. **gas**	

B. Complete the story with words from the chart.

   We did a great experiment last week. We changed the state of water. First we

put water in the freezer. After two hours, the water became solid ice. We had learned

to _____ water! Then our teacher heated the water until it became

steam. We had learned how to _____ water! Last we let ice melt in a

pan. The ice changed from solid to liquid. We had learned to _____ ice!

Vocabulary: Science, SV 9781419034992

Name _____ Date _____

The Language of Testing

How would you answer a question like this on a test?

Choose the (best) answer. What is the measure of the amount of matter in a substance?

Ⓐ mass
Ⓑ weight
Ⓒ volume
Ⓓ density

Tip

When *best* is used in the directions, it means *most correct*. More than one answer might be slightly correct, but only one answer is the most correct or best.

Test Strategy: If you see a question asking for the *best* answer, rewrite it using the phrase *most correct*.

1. How could you say the question above in a different way?

   _____

   _____

Try the strategy again by asking these questions in a different way.

2. What are three states of matter?

   Ⓐ density, mass, and volume
   Ⓑ solid, liquid, gas
   Ⓒ solid, liquid, mass
   Ⓓ solid, mass, volume

3. What two states of matter generally have the greatest volume?

   Ⓐ gas and solid
   Ⓑ liquid and solid
   Ⓒ liquid and gas
   Ⓓ all of the above

Name _____ Date _____

On Your Own

Answer the questions.

1. What are some things that are made of **atoms**? _____

_____

2. How can you tell the **density** of something? _____

_____

3. What are some common **gases**? _____

_____

4. Name some drinkable **liquids**. _____

_____

5. How can you find the **mass** of something? _____

_____

6. What is **matter** made of? _____

_____

7. What **solids** can you eat? _____

_____

8. How can you measure **volume**? _____

_____

Write On!

You are a scientist experimenting with the three states of matter. You've made an amazing discovery. On another sheet of paper, describe your discovery in your journal. Be sure to include at least three details about your discovery. Use four or more words from the lesson correctly.

atom	density	mass	matter	gas
solid	liquid	volume	order	general

Name _____ Date _____

Lesson 12 Assessment

Read the sentences. Look for the best word to complete each sentence. Fill in the circle for the answer you choose. The first one has been done for you.

1. There are three states of _____.
   - (A) liquid
   - (B) gas
   - **(C) matter**
   - (D) solid

2. The _____ of something tells how much matter it contains.
   - (A) atom
   - (B) mass
   - (C) matter
   - (D) order

3. Oxygen and hydrogen are examples of _____.
   - (A) liquids
   - (B) atoms
   - (C) gases
   - (D) solids

4. _____ are the smallest part of anything.
   - (A) Gases
   - (B) Liquids
   - (C) Solids
   - (D) Atoms

5. An atom's nucleus has _____.
   - (A) density
   - (B) gases
   - (C) cells
   - (D) liquids

6. When water turns to ice, it becomes a _____.
   - (A) liquid
   - (B) solid
   - (C) gas
   - (D) volume

7. When ice turns to water, it becomes a _____.
   - (A) solid
   - (B) gas
   - (C) volume
   - (D) liquid

8. When you measure the _____ of something, you find out how much space it takes up.
   - (A) weight
   - (B) order
   - (C) volume
   - (D) matter

9. In _____, the weather forecaster's predictions were wrong last week.
   - (A) order
   - (B) general
   - (C) volume
   - (D) matter

10. Gas has no shape because the atoms of gas have no _____ in the way they move.
    - (A) volume
    - (B) matter
    - (C) mass
    - (D) order

Lesson 12: Matter
Vocabulary: Science, SV 9781419034992

Name _____ Date _____

Energy

Read the passage below. Think about the meanings of the new words printed in **bold**. Circle any definitions that might help you figure out what these words mean. Draw an arrow from the definition to the word it describes. The first one has been done for you.

 Ben Franklin

Using a simple kite, Ben Franklin showed that lightning is **electricity**, a kind of energy. Franklin's experiments with electricity went far beyond his kite, however. He made **batteries** to create and store electricity. He was also interested in **static**, a buildup of electricity on an object. You know static as the "shock" you sometimes get from a doorknob. Franklin built machines that would create static electricity. Through those machines, he learned about **conduction**, or how electricity moves from place to place.

Franklin also created the lightning rod. A lightning rod is a tall pole with a wire that goes down to the ground. A lightning rod is placed on the roof of a building to prevent lightning from starting fires. When lightning hits the rod, it moves down the wire and hits the ground. Franklin made the first lightning rod in 1750. Today, lightning rods still protect thousands of buildings.

Vocabulary Strategy

Look for definitions in the text to help you understand the meanings of new words.

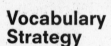 **New Science Words**

battery

noun an object that uses water and other materials to store electricity

electricity

noun a form of energy used for lighting, heating, and powering machines

conduction

noun how heat and energy move through something

static

noun a buildup of energy on an object

Name _____ Date _____

Now read this passage and practice the vocabulary strategy again. Circle any definitions in the passage that help you figure out what the new words in **bold** mean. Draw an arrow from the definition to the word it describes.

 Power Up!

There are hundreds of wires in your home. These wires bring electrical **current** to different parts of your house or apartment. Current is the movement of electricity. Electricity travels in a **circuit**, which is a complete path. When a circuit breaks, the flow of electricity stops. That's what happens when you turn off a light switch. A light switch is **designed**, or made, in such a way as to break a circuit.

It is hard to imagine what it would be like to live without electricity. It can be used to light our homes, **heat** them with warm air, or even cool them with fans and air conditioners. Electricity runs our radios and computers. Still, with all these good uses, electricity also has the **potential** to be dangerous. It can start fires. It can also shock, or hurt someone badly. Remember to be safe with electricity.

 More New Science Words

circuit
  noun   a complete and closed path that electricity can flow through
current
  noun   a steady movement of water, air, or electricity
heat
  noun   warmth or being hot
potential
  noun   something that is possible but isn't yet real
  adjective   possible, but not yet real

When Ben Franklin said there was **electricity** in the air, they told him to "go fly a kite."

 Other Useful Words

design
  verb   to plan and make something to look a certain way or to do something specific
figure
  noun   a picture that shows information about something
  verb   to solve a problem

 Use the Strategy

Look at a chapter in your textbook that your teacher identifies. Use definitions in the text to help you figure out the meaning of any new words you find.

Name _____ Date _____

Finish the sentences in Group A with words from Group B. Write the letter of the word on the line.

Group A

1. I got a shock from the metal doorknob because of the _____, or buildup of energy on it.

2. Cars, flashlights, and some radios get their power from _____.

3. The _____ from the campfire felt good in the chilly evening.

4. We used math to _____ out, or solve, the problem.

Group B

A. batteries
B. figure
C. static
D. heat

Group A

5. Our project was to _____ a box that would protect an egg from being crushed.

6. The clouds in the sky meant that there was a _____ for rain.

7. Ben Franklin proved that lightning was a form of _____.

8. The electrical _____ moved through the wire.

Group B

E. design
F. electricity
G. current
H. potential

Name _____ Date _____

Word Challenge: Finish the Idea

Read the incomplete sentences below. Write an ending for each. The first one has been done for you.

1. We knew the **circuit** was broken because _the lights and the TV turned off._____

2. I like having things that use **batteries** for power because _____

   _____

3. My favorite team had a good **potential** to win many games this season because

   _____

4. I would like to **design** _____ because _____

   _____

Word Challenge: What's Your Answer?

Read each question and write an answer on the line. Answer the questions in complete sentences. The first one has been done for you.

1. What does it mean if something improves **conduction**?

   It means that electricity can move through it better._____

2. What would you miss if there were no **electricity**? _____

   _____

3. When do you like to have **heat**? _____

   _____

4. How would you **figure** out a hard problem? _____

   _____

Lesson 13: Energy
Vocabulary: Science, SV 9781419034992

Name _____   Date _____

 Same or Opposite

In each of the groups, circle the two words that mean the same or almost the same as each other.

1. potential   real

design   possible

3. heat   warmth

electricity   water

2. battery   path

circuit   plug

4. power   electricity

design   general

 Word Study: The Suffix -al

When the suffix -al is added to a word such as education, it changes the word's meaning.
- First, it makes the word an adjective: educational.
- Second, it adds "connected to" to the word's meaning.

education (n.) learning and teaching
educational (adj.) connected to learning and teaching

A. Add the -al suffix to make a new word. Write your own definitions for each. Use a dictionary to check your spelling and definitions.

	+ -al	Meaning
1. **electric**		
2. **figure**		
3. **potent** (powerful)		

B. Complete each sentence with an -al word from the chart.

1. Something that has to do with a drawing or picture is _____.

2. If something has the power to do something, it has _____.

3. A clock that is powered by electricity is _____.

Lesson 13: Energy
Vocabulary: Science, SV 9781419034992

Name _____ Date _____

The Language of Testing

How would you answer a question like this on a test?

What conclusion can be drawn from the following clues? <u>You plug a lamp in, there is a popping sound, and all the lights go out.</u>

Ⓐ There is an electrical storm.
Ⓑ Lightning has struck the house.
Ⓒ The circuit for the room is broken.
Ⓓ You forgot to pay your electric bill.

Tip

When *what conclusion can be drawn* is used in the directions, it means *what happened?* or *why did this happen?* You must choose the best possible reason from the choices given.

Test Strategy: If you see *what conclusion can be drawn* in a test question, place the phrases *what happened?* or *why did this happen?* after the event described.

1. How could you say the question above in a different way?

_____

_____

Try the strategy again by asking these questions in a different way.

2. What conclusion can be drawn from the following event? A flashlight battery works for a short time, but it is dim. Then it goes out.

Ⓐ The lightbulb has gone bad.
Ⓑ You need a new flashlight.
Ⓒ The battery is weak.
Ⓓ The flashlight wasn't made well.

_____

_____

_____

_____

3. An electrician discovers that two wires are not connected. What conclusion can be drawn from this information?

Ⓐ The circuit is not working.
Ⓑ The electrician made a mistake.
Ⓒ The wiring needs to be checked.
Ⓓ All of the above

_____

_____

_____

_____

Lesson 13: Energy
Vocabulary: Science, SV 9781419034992

Name _____ Date _____

Answer the questions.

1. What things need **batteries**? _____

_____

2. What happens in a **circuit**? _____

_____

3. Where does **conduction** happen? _____

_____

4. What things move in a **current**? _____

_____

5. What can you use **electricity** to do? _____

_____

6. What things create or give off **heat**? _____

_____

7. How can you measure **potential**? _____

_____

8. What causes **static**? _____

_____

Write On!

You are Ben Franklin's assistant on the day he "discovers" electricity. On another sheet of paper, write a conversation between the two of you on that day. Give at least three details of the discovery. Use four or more words from the lesson correctly.

| conduction | static | figure | potential | heat |
| circuit | design | current | battery | electricity |

Name _____ Date _____

Lesson 13 Assessment

Read the sentences. Look for the best word to complete each sentence. Fill in the circle for the answer you choose. The first one has been done for you.

1. _____ can store electricity.
   Ⓐ Conduction
   🅑 Batteries
   Ⓒ Heat
   Ⓓ Circuits

2. Electricity moves through _____.
   Ⓐ heat
   Ⓑ conduction
   Ⓒ figures
   Ⓓ potential

3. _____ is a form of energy.
   Ⓐ A battery
   Ⓑ Conduction
   Ⓒ Electricity
   Ⓓ A circuit

4. Inventors have the _____ to make our lives better.
   Ⓐ conduction
   Ⓑ currents
   Ⓒ circuits
   Ⓓ potential

5. A _____ is always a closed path.
   Ⓐ circuit
   Ⓑ current
   Ⓒ battery
   Ⓓ conduction

6. Water, air, and electricity have _____.
   Ⓐ conductions
   Ⓑ currents
   Ⓒ batteries
   Ⓓ static

7. You might feel _____ when you touch a metal object.
   Ⓐ batteries
   Ⓑ conduction
   Ⓒ potential
   Ⓓ static

8. Many people use electricity to _____ their homes.
   Ⓐ design
   Ⓑ heat
   Ⓒ figure
   Ⓓ conduct

9. John has _____ a house that uses only solar energy.
   Ⓐ figured
   Ⓑ conducted
   Ⓒ designed
   Ⓓ conserved

10. The new _____ shows a plan for conserving electricity.
    Ⓐ circuit
    Ⓑ current
    Ⓒ conduction
    Ⓓ figure

Lesson 13: Energy
Vocabulary: Science, SV 9781419034992

Forces and Motion

Read the passage below. Think about the meanings of the new words printed in **bold**. Underline any examples or descriptions you find that might help you figure out what these words mean. The first one has been done for you.

Isaac Newton

Isaac Newton was one of the greatest scientists of all time. He discovered **gravity**. He figured out that Earth's gravity pulls harder on larger objects than smaller ones. That's why a small stone weighs less than a large one. Gravity was just one **force** that Newton described. An example of a force would be a push or a pull.

Newton also described how forces work with **motion**. An example of this would be how a wagon moves. He said that unless a force is **applied**, or used with something, it will not move. He also said that once an object was in motion, it would stay in motion until something stopped it. Usually **friction** causes an object to stop moving, like the brakes on a car.

In high school you may take a math course called calculus. You can blame Newton for that. He created it!

New Science Words

force	**gravity**
noun something that moves or changes something	*noun* what causes things to fall toward the ground when dropped
friction	
noun something that stops one object from moving against another	**motion**
	noun movement
	verb to make a movement

www.harcourtschoolsupply.com
110
Lesson 14: Forces and Motion
Vocabulary: Science, SV 9781419034992

Name _____ Date _____

Now read this passage and practice the vocabulary strategy again. Underline the examples and descriptions in the passage. Draw an arrow from each to the word it describes.

Sailors Long Ago

How did sailors long ago figure out the **position** of their boat in the ocean? For example, they could have been a few miles east of Florida. How did they know? Also, how did they know which direction they were heading in?

Before tools were invented to help them, sailors used the stars. Then about a thousand years ago, Chinese sailors began using **magnets** to find direction. You might know that a magnet can pick up pieces of metal. The **poles**, or opposite ends of the magnet, line up with the North Pole, too. This is how a magnet can help you find your direction.

Sailors need to know their position and the direction they are going in so that they can give **instructions** to their crew to avoid dangers in the water. These instructions might be "head south!" or "watch out for the rocks!" If a ship hits rock or sand, it has to be moved into deeper waters. Sailors use ropes and **levers** that look like big seesaws to pull and push the ship back into the water.

 More New Science Words

lever
noun a bar used to lift a heavy object

magnet
noun a piece of metal that can attract some types of metal

poles
noun the opposite, or positive and negative, ends of a magnet

position
noun place or location

 Other Useful Words

apply
verb to use what you know

instructions
noun information that explains how to do something

"I think our exact **position** is at the North Pole, sir."

Use the Strategy

Look at a chapter in your textbook that your teacher identifies. Use examples, descriptions, and pictures in the text to help you figure out the meaning of any new words you find.

Name _____ Date _____

 Finish the Paragraph

Use the words in **bold** to finish the paragraph below. Write the correct word on the line. One word will not be used.

force   **friction**   **gravity**   **magnets**   **motion**   **pole**   **position**

Scientists have designed a train that floats above its tracks. It looks like it is not

affected by _____. The trains and tracks have very powerful
                          1

_____ that hold the train in _____ about four
            2   **3**

inches above the track. When the trains are in _____, they can
                                                              4

travel at speeds over 300 miles per hour! The trains float above the tracks, so there isn't

_____ from wheels rubbing against the rails. Because of this, it
            5

takes very little _____ to move these trains. Full-sized trains are
                              6

being used in some countries. Someday

you might ride on one of these fast

magnetic trains.

Name _____ Date _____

Word Challenge: True or False

Write **T** next to each sentence that is true. Write **F** next to each sentence that is false. Rewrite the false sentences. The first one has been done for you.

1. __T__ A **force** is something that pushes or pulls something else.

2. _____ If you had to move a large rock, you would not need a **lever**.

_____

3. _____ **Gravity** causes objects to float off into space.

_____

4. _____ When you **apply** your knowledge to solve a problem, you don't use anything

you have learned.

_____

Word Challenge: Which Word?

Think of a statement for each word below that gives a strong clue about its meaning. Write your statement next to the word. The first one has been done for you.

1. **friction** _"I can stop a train in its tracks!"_

2. **position** _____

3. **pole** _____

4. **instructions** _____

Lesson 14: Forces and Motion
Vocabulary: Science, SV 9781419034992

Name _____ Date _____

Extend the Meaning

Write the letter of the word or phrase that best completes each sentence.

1. You can find your **position** by _____.
a. looking at the ground
b. using a compass
c. looking behind you

2. You can test a **magnet** by _____.
a. touching it to iron or steel
b. its shape
c. finding its poles

3. You might use a **lever** to _____.
a. dig a hole
b. build a bridge
c. help move a stuck car

4. The **poles** of a magnet are _____.
a. always flat
b. opposites
c. always labeled

Word Study: The Suffixes -ation and -tion

When the suffix -ation or -tion is added to a verb such as *locate*, two things happen:
- First, it makes the word a noun: *location*.
- Second, it changes the word's meaning. The word now means "the place where something is."

locate (v.) to find or to place something
location (n.) the place where something is

A. Add the suffix -ation or -tion to make a new word. Use a dictionary to check your spelling.

	Definition	+ -ation or -tion
1. gravitate	to move toward something	
2. posit	to place something somewhere	
3. apply	to use what you know	

B. Write a new -ation or -tion word on each line.

1. I posited the book on the shelf so I will know its _____ when I need to find it.

2. Myra wanted to apply for a job, so she asked for an _____.

3. Dead leaves gravitate to the ground. I think it's because of Earth's _____.

Lesson 14: Forces and Motion
Vocabulary: Science, SV 9781419034992

Name _____   Date _____

The Language of Testing

How would you answer a question like this on a test?

What is the (**major cause**) of heat in the brakes of a car?

- Ⓐ the car's speed
- Ⓑ friction
- Ⓒ the heat of the roadway
- Ⓓ the outside air temperature

The phrase *major cause* means *the most important reason for something.*

Test Strategy: If the question has the phrase *major cause* in it, restate the question using *most important reason for*. You can also add the phrase *is a major cause of . . .* to each answer choice to see if it is right or wrong.

1. What phrase would you use to test each answer choice above?

_____

_____

Try the strategy again by adding a test phrase to the answer choices below. Write your test phrase below each question.

2. What is a major cause of earthquakes?

- Ⓐ the shifting of the earth's crust
- Ⓑ volcanic eruptions
- Ⓒ ocean tides
- Ⓓ underground explosions

3. Choose a major cause of electrical fires.

- Ⓐ too many electrical lines
- Ⓑ faulty wiring
- Ⓒ lightning
- Ⓓ bad fuses

Lesson 14: Forces and Motion
Vocabulary: Science, SV 9781419034992

Name _____ Date _____

 On Your Own

Answer the questions.

1. What **forces** do you use when you play ball? _____

_____

2. Describe how **friction** works. _____

_____

3. What would happen if there was no **gravity**? _____

_____

4. How can a **lever** help you do work? _____

_____

5. What are some ways to use a **magnet**? _____

_____

6. How can you measure **motion**? _____

_____

7. Where are Earth's two **poles**? _____

_____

8. What can the **position** of something tell you? _____

_____

Write On!

You are a crew member of a ship sailing into unexplored waters a long time ago. On another sheet of paper, write a short descriptive article with at least three details of how the crew found its way. Use four or more words from the lesson correctly.

force	motion	friction	gravity	lever
apply	position	pole	magnet	instructions

Name _____ Date _____

Lesson 14 Assessment

Read the sentences. Look for the best word to complete each sentence. Fill in the circle for the answer you choose. The first one has been done for you.

1. _____ slows an object that is in motion.
   (A) A pole
   (B) Position
   (C) Friction
   (D) A magnet

2. You need to apply _____ to make something move.
   (A) motion
   (B) force
   (C) gravity
   (D) friction

3. _____ can be used to lift heavy objects.
   (A) Levers
   (B) Poles
   (C) Friction
   (D) Gravity

4. Long ago, sailors followed the stars to find their _____ at sea.
   (A) levers
   (B) poles
   (C) magnets
   (D) position

5. _____ makes things fall to the ground.
   (A) Motion
   (B) A magnet
   (C) Gravity
   (D) A pole

6. _____ can help you find your direction.
   (A) Poles
   (B) Magnets
   (C) Levers
   (D) Gravity

7. _____ are at opposite ends of a magnet or the earth.
   (A) Magnets
   (B) Levers
   (C) Forces
   (D) Poles

8. Newton said you have to _____ a force to something to make it move.
   (A) notice
   (B) compare
   (C) apply
   (D) measure

9. _____ happens when something changes its position.
   (A) Force
   (B) Motion
   (C) Apply
   (D) Gravity

10. Jim doesn't do well in school because he refuses to follow _____.
    (A) positions
    (B) motion
    (C) instructions
    (D) friction

Name _____ Date _____

Sound and Light

Read the passage below. Think about the meanings of the new words printed in **bold**. Create connections between the new words and words you know. These will help you remember what the new words mean. Mark or write these connections near the new words in the passage. The first one has been done for you.

 ## A Trick of the Light?

Vocabulary Strategy

Create connections between new words and words you know. You can use a Word Anchor chart to help you create connections.

Optics is the study of how light works and how we see. People have been interested in optics for thousands of years. As early as 200 BCE, Greek thinkers studied how (mirrors) could **reflect** light, bouncing it back in different ways. Legend has it that one person used a mirror to win a battle. He reflected the sun's **rays** into the eyes of the enemy. The bright, narrow flashes of light blinded them.

Early scientists also experimented with **prisms**, which separated light into different colors, like a rainbow.

Around CE 1200, people began to focus light through a **lens**, a thin piece of curved glass. They found that the shape of a lens could make an image look larger or smaller. A thicker lens that curves outward on both sides makes a larger image. A thinner lens that curves inward on both sides makes a smaller one.

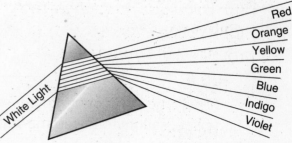

White Light — Red, Orange, Yellow, Green, Blue, Indigo, Violet

New Science Words

lens

noun   a piece of clear glass or plastic that is curved on one or both sides

prism

noun   a clear piece of glass or plastic that is shaped like a triangle and separates light into colors

ray

noun   a narrow beam of light

reflect

verb   to bounce light, sound, or heat off an object

118

Name _____ Date _____

Now read this passage and practice the vocabulary strategy again. Write near or mark in the text any connections you can use to help you "anchor" the meaning of new words.

 ## Guitar Strings

Do you like to listen to rock music? Most rock bands **include**, or have, one or more guitar players. The strings of those guitars can teach us something about sound. When a player strums the guitar, the strings start to **vibrate**. As the strings move back and forth very fast, they create sound that we can hear. In fact, this movement is actually **visible** if you look at the string.

The highness or lowness of the sound, or **pitch**, depends on the length of the string. As a guitar player moves his or her fingers up and down the neck of the guitar, the vibrating part of the string gets shorter or longer. The sound from the shorter string is higher. The longer string makes a lower pitch. Guitars are built to make the sound of the strings clear and loud. They use wood and other materials that will not **absorb** the sound like a sponge absorbs water.

 ## More New Science Words

absorb
verb   to soak up something

pitch
noun   the highness or lowness of a sound

vibrate
verb   to move back and forth very quickly

visible
adjective   seen by the human eye

Arturo thought that sponges would **absorb** the sound of Kelley's horrible music.

 ## Other Useful Words

include
verb   to make one or more things part of something else

prove
noun   to show something is true or real

 ## Use the Strategy

Look at a chapter in your textbook that your teacher identifies. Use associations to help you anchor your understanding of any new words you find.

Vocabulary: Science, SV 9781419034992

Name _____ Date _____

The Right Word

Read each sentence. Look at the word or phrase that is underlined. Write one of the words from the box that means the same or almost the same thing as the underlined part of the sentence.

lenses	prism	rays	reflected

1. _____ They had to replace the <u>curved pieces of glass</u> in my glasses because they were scratched.

2. _____ <u>Narrow beams of light</u> from the afternoon sun came in through the window.

3. _____ The trees on the shore <u>sent back an image</u> off the still water of the lake.

4. _____ The light that came through the <u>clear piece of glass shaped like a triangle</u> made colors on the wall.

absorb	pitch	vibrate	visible

5. _____ We used paper towels to <u>soak up</u> the water that was spilled on the floor.

6. _____ The singer couldn't find the right <u>highness or lowness of sound</u> and sounded horrible.

7. _____ The lights of the city were <u>seen by the human eye</u> from many miles away.

8. _____ We could feel the engine <u>move very quickly back and forth</u> as soon as the old car started.

Vocabulary: Science, SV 9781419034992

Name _____ Date _____

Word Challenge: Describe the Scene

Read each question and write an answer on the line. Answer the questions in complete sentences. The first one has been done for you.

1. The padding on the walls **absorbed** the sound of the music. How did the

   music sound? _The music sounded very quiet and muffled._

2. The blinds were closed, but a **ray** of sun came through. What did the sunlight

   look like? _____

   _____

3. The flowers in the backyard were **reflected** in the mirror. What could you see?

   _____

4. You want to **prove** to your friends that you know a hard skateboard trick. What do

   you do? _____

   _____

Word Challenge: Finish the Idea

Read the incomplete sentences below. Write an ending for each. The first one has been done for you.

1. The guitar string **vibrated** because _the player plucked it._

2. The white light went through the **prism** and _____

   _____

3. We knew the trumpet was off **pitch** because _____

   _____

4. We did not **include** his brother in our game because _____

   _____

Vocabulary: Science, SV 9781419034992

Name _____ Date _____

Categories

Write the words from the word bank in the correct boxes below. Two words may be used in both boxes.

absorb	lens	pitch	prism	ray	reflect	vibrate	visible

Sound Words	Light Words

Word Study: The Root *vis*

The root *vis* means *see*. You can add many prefixes and suffixes to *vis* to make new words.

vis (root) to see
visible (adj.) able to be seen
invisible (adj.) unable to be seen

Add the prefixes and suffixes to *vis* to make new words. Provide definitions for the words you create. Use a dictionary to check your spelling and definitions.

1. *vis + ual =* _____ Means _____

_____

2. *vis + ual + ize =* _____ Means _____

_____

3. *visible + ity =* _____ Means _____

_____

4. *in + visible + ity =* _____ Means _____

_____

Name _____ Date _____

The Language of Testing

How would you answer a question like this on a test?

What was the result when the length of the vibrating string was shortened?

    (A) The pitch became lower.
    (B) The pitch became higher.
    (C) The sound was softer.
    (D) The sound was louder.

Tip

The phrase *what was the result* can also mean *what happened after*.

Test Strategy: If you see a question that uses the phrase *what was the result*, rewrite it using the phrase *what happened after*.

1. How could you say the question above in a different way?

_____

_____

Try the strategy again by asking these questions in a different way.

2. What was the result when the light passed through a concave lens?

    (A) The image became smaller.
    (B) The image became larger.
    (C) The light was broken into different colors.
    (D) The image was reversed.

_____

_____

_____

_____

3. What was the result when layers of newspaper were wrapped around the speaker?

    (A) The sound was improved.
    (B) The low pitches became clearer.
    (C) The sound was absorbed.
    (D) The high pitches became clearer.

_____

_____

_____

_____

Lesson 15: Sound and Light
Vocabulary: Science, SV 9781419034992

Name _____ Date _____

On Your Own

Answer the questions.

1. What are some things that **absorb**? _____

   _____

2. Where would you find a **lens**? _____

   _____

3. How can you measure **pitch**? _____

   _____

4. What can a **prism** be used for? _____

   _____

5. What things give off **rays**? _____

   _____

6. What things **reflect** light? _____

   _____

7. What can cause something to **vibrate**? _____

   _____

8. What are some things that are not **visible**? _____

   _____

Write On!

On another sheet of paper, write a conversation between a nature photographer who needs quiet to take pictures and a musician who needs to practice loud music in the same spot where the photographer is working. Each should try to persuade the other, with at least two reasons, to stop working. Use four or more words from the lesson correctly.

include	pitch	absorb	prism	lens
ray	reflect	prove	vibrate	visible

Lesson 15: Sound and Light
Vocabulary: Science, SV 9781419034992

Name _____ Date _____

Lesson 15 Assessment

Read the sentences. Look for the best word to complete each sentence. Fill in the circle for the answer you choose. The first one has been done for you.

1. What would you _____ in a model of a lens?
   - Ⓐ reflect
   - Ⓑ absorb
   - Ⓒ vibrate
   - Ⓓ include

2. Scientists must _____ their hypotheses.
   - Ⓐ include
   - Ⓑ prove
   - Ⓒ absorb
   - Ⓓ reflect

3. A sponge can _____ a lot of water.
   - Ⓐ vibrate
   - Ⓑ include
   - Ⓒ absorb
   - Ⓓ reflect

4. When guitar strings make sound, they _____.
   - Ⓐ reflect
   - Ⓑ absorb
   - Ⓒ recycle
   - Ⓓ vibrate

5. The _____ in a telescope is a piece of curved glass.
   - Ⓐ lens
   - Ⓑ prism
   - Ⓒ ray
   - Ⓓ pitch

6. A _____ separates light into colors.
   - Ⓐ vibrate
   - Ⓑ ray
   - Ⓒ prism
   - Ⓓ pitch

7. A _____ is a beam of light.
   - Ⓐ pitch
   - Ⓑ lens
   - Ⓒ prism
   - Ⓓ ray

8. A musical instrument might make sounds with a high or low _____.
   - Ⓐ prism
   - Ⓑ ray
   - Ⓒ pitch
   - Ⓓ lens

9. Mirrors can _____ light.
   - Ⓐ vibrate
   - Ⓑ reflect
   - Ⓒ absorb
   - Ⓓ include

10. Some things are only _____ if you look at them through a microscope.
    - Ⓐ reflected
    - Ⓑ visible
    - Ⓒ vibrated
    - Ⓓ included

Lesson 15: Sound and Light
Vocabulary: Science, SV 9781419034992

Answer Key

page 8
1. control
2. experiment
3. graph
4. hypothesis
5. theory
6. model
7. law
8. chart
9. scientist
Puzzle Answer: nightmare

page 9
Word Challenge:
Correct or Incorrect
1. C
2. I; Anya made a graph (or chart) to show how much her dog has grown.
3. C
4. C
Word Challenge:
Which Word?
Answers will vary.

page 10
Extend the Meaning
1. b   3. a
2. a   4. b
Word Study
1. experimenting, to perform a scientific test to prove something
2. graphing, to make a drawing that compares numbers or amounts
3. modeling, to make a copy of something to show its details
4. controlling, to have power over something

page 11
Answers to restated questions will vary.
Check students' responses.
1. C   2. D   3. B

page 12
Answers will vary.

page 13
1. C   6. C
2. C   7. D
3. B   8. A
4. D   9. B
5. A   10. C

page 16
1. adapt
2. reproduce
3. simple
4. cells
5. classified
6. nucleus
7. form
8. divide

page 17
Word Challenge:
Finish the Idea
Answers will vary.
Word Challenge:
What's Your Answer?
Answers will vary.

page 18
Extend the Meaning
1. d   3. a
2. c   4. b
Word Study
A. 1. reform, to make something again
   2. reclassify, to sort things into groups by how they are alike again
   3. reproduce, to make a copy of something or to produce young
B. 1. reproduce
   2. reform

page 19
Answers to restated questions will vary.
Check students' responses.
1. C   2. A   3. D

page 20
Answers will vary.

page 21
1. B   6. D
2. C   7. B
3. D   8. A
4. A   9. B
5. C   10. C

page 24
1. C   5. E
2. B   6. G
3. A   7. F
4. D   8. H

page 25
Word Challenge:
True or False
1. F; Sprouts grow on top of the ground.
2. F; The leaf is part of a plant that is flat, thin, and green.
3. T
4. F; Plants make energy with photosynthesis.
Word Challenge:
Which Word?
Answers will vary.

page 26
Finish the Idea
Answers will vary.
Word Study
A. 1. leafless, without leaves
   2. rootless, without roots
   3. seedless, without seeds
B. 1. leafless
   2. seedless
   3. rootless

page 27
Answers to restated questions will vary.
Check students' responses.
1. C   2. B   3. A

page 28
Answers will vary.

page 29
1. D   6. B
2. B   7. D
3. C   8. B
4. A   9. C
5. C   10. A

page 32
1. amphibians
2. hatch
3. reptile
4. mammals
5. dinosaur

page 33
Word Challenge:
Correct or Incorrect
1. I; Vertebrates have backbones.
2. I; Reptiles are cold-blooded and don't make their own heat.

3. I; Only female animals have ovaries.
4. C
Word Challenge:
Example/Not an Example
Answers will vary.

page 34
Analogies
1. reptile
2. amphibian
3. embryo
4. dinosaur
Word Study
A. 1. mammalian
   2. ovarian
   3. reptilian
B. 1. mammalian
   2. reptilian

page 35
Answers to restated questions will vary.
Check students' responses.
1. B   2. A   3. C

page 36
Answers will vary.

page 37
1. A   6. A
2. C   7. D
3. D   8. C
4. B   9. B
5. C   10. B

page 40
1. cycle
2. role
3. nutrients
4. consume
5. energy
6. decay
7. relationship
Puzzle answer: Let's eat!

page 41
Word Challenge:
Which Word?
Answers will vary.
Word Challenge:
What's Your Answer?
Answers will vary.

page 42
Word Connections
Yes: decay, energy, nutrients
No: cycle, cause, example
Word Study
A. 1. consume, -able
   2. produce, -ible

B. 1. producible
   2. consumable

page 43
Answers to restated questions will vary. Check students' responses.
1. B   **2.** A   **3.** C

page 44
Answers will vary.

page 45
1. C   **6.** B
2. B   **7.** A
3. A   **8.** C
4. C   **9.** D
5. D   **10.** C

page 48
1. population
2. examined
3. desert
4. tropical
5. habitat
6. method
7. forest
8. environment

page 49
Word Challenge:
True or False
1. F; A tropical climate is usually very warm and wet.
2. T
3. F; A forest has many trees.
4. F; The habitat of fish is in a body of water.
Word Challenge:
What's Your Answer?
Answers will vary.

page 50
Analogies
1. desert
2. forest
3. tropical or desert
4. examine
Word Study
A. intercommunity, interecosystem, interforest, interdesert
B. 1. interdesert
   2. interforest
   3. interecosystem

page 51
Answers to restated questions will vary. Check students' responses.
1. B   **2.** C   **3.** A

page 52
Answers will vary.

page 53
1. D   **6.** D
2. C   **7.** B
3. B   **8.** C
4. C   **9.** D
5. A   **10.** C

page 56
1. fossil   **5.** recorded
2. core   **6.** crust
3. oxygen   **7.** carbon
4. mineral   **8.** mantle

page 57
Word Challenge:
Which Word?
Answers will vary.
Word Challenge:
Correct or Incorrect
1. I; We made a drawing showing the earth's center, the core.
2. I; Some of Earth's minerals are salt, iron, and silver.
3. C
4. C

page 58
Word Pairs
1. oxygen, nitrogen
2. Carbon, mineral
3. mantle, core
4. record, conduct
Word Study
A. 1. oxygenation, the process or result of adding oxygen
   2. nitrogenation, the process or result of adding nitrogen
   3. carbonation, the process or result of adding carbon
B. 1. carbonation
   2. oxygenation

page 59
Answers to restated questions will vary. Check students' responses.
1. C   **2.** C   **3.** A

page 60
Answers will vary.

page 61
1. B   **6.** A
2. C   **7.** D
3. D   **8.** C
4. C   **9.** A
5. D   **10.** B

page 64
1. B   **5.** H
2. D   **6.** E
3. A   **7.** G
4. C   **8.** F

page 65
Word Challenge:
Finish the Idea
Answers will vary.
Word Challenge:
What's Your Answer?
Answers will vary.

page 66
Word Pairs
1. sediment, erosion
2. continent, glacier
3. earthquake, surface
4. volcano, lava
Word Study
A. 1. sedimentology, sedimentologist
   2. volcanology, volcanologist
B. Answers will vary.

page 67
1. because of the flooding; D
2. because of the Ice Age; C
3. because of water freezing and melting; A

page 68
Answers will vary.

page 69
1. C   **6.** B
2. B   **7.** D
3. C   **8.** C
4. D   **9.** B
5. C   **10.** C

page 72
1. exploring   **6.** solar
2. planets   **7.** lunar
3. orbits   **8.** phases
4. satellite   **9.** measure
5. axis

page 73
Word Challenge:
Finish the Idea
Answers will vary.
Word Challenge:
True or False
1. T
2. F; A normal orbit is curved.
3. F; During each phase, the moon looks different.
4. T

page 74
Word Connections
Yes: lunar, orbit, satellite
No: axis, planet, solar
Word Study
A. 1. nonsolar, having nothing to do with the sun
   2. nonexample, not an example
   3. nonsense, without sense
B. Answers will vary.

page 75
Answers to restated questions will vary. Check students' responses.
1. C   **2.** A   **3.** B

page 76
Answers will vary.

page 77
1. D   **6.** B
2. B   **7.** C
3. C   **8.** D
4. D   **9.** C
5. A   **10.** A

page 80
1. humidity
2. thermometer
3. front
4. pressure
5. climate
6. label
7. temperature
8. predict

page 81
Word Challenge: Would You Rather...
Answers will vary.
Word Challenge: Word Relationships
1. thermometer
2. pressure
3. evaporation
4. temperature

page 82
Extend the Meaning
1. c   **3.** c
2. b   **4.** a
Word Study
A. 1. labeled, to have placed a name on something
   2. predicted, to have said what will happen
   3. pressured, to have pushed on something
B. predicted, labeled

Answer Key
Vocabulary: Science, SV 9781419034992

page 83

Answers to restated questions will vary. Check students' responses.

1. B   2. A   3. D

page 84

Answers will vary.

page 85

1. B   6. B
2. B   7. A
3. A   8. B
4. C   9. C
5. D   10. C

page 88

1. a   5. b
2. b   6. a
3. c   7. b
4. b   8. c

page 89

Word Challenge:
Example/Not an Example

Answers will vary.

Word Challenge:
What's Your Reason?

Answers will vary.

page 90

What's the Answer?

1. a, b   3. a, c
2. b   4. b

Word Study

1. extractor, a person that takes something out of something else
2. polluter, a person that dirties and harms the water, soil, and air
3. recycler, a person that uses something over again
4. communicator, a person that shares information through speaking, writing, or movements

page 91

Answers to restated questions will vary. Check students' responses.

1. A
2. No answer can be given; check only restatement of question.
3. No answer can be given; check only restatement of question.

page 92

Answers will vary.

page 93

1. D   6. B
2. B   7. D
3. A   8. C
4. C   9. B
5. C   10. C

page 96

1. liquid   5. gas
2. matter   6. atom
3. solid   7. order
4. volume   8. general

page 97

Word Challenge:
Which Word?

Answers will vary.

Word Challenge:
Correct or Incorrect

1. I; There are three states of matter.
2. I; The mass of an object is how much matter it has inside it.
3. C
4. I; Her interests are so general that she has many hobbies.

page 98

Analogies

1. solid   3. general
2. atom   4. liquid

Word Study

A. 1. solidify
   2. liquefy
   3. gasify
B. solidify, gasify, liquefy

page 99

Answers to restated questions will vary. Check students' responses.

1. A   2. B   3. C

page 100

Answers will vary.

page 101

1. C   6. B
2. B   7. D
3. C   8. C
4. D   9. B
5. A   10. D

page 104

1. C   5. E
2. A   6. H
3. D   7. F
4. B   8. G

page 105

Word Challenge:
Finish the Idea

Answers will vary.

Word Challenge:
What's Your Answer?

Answers will vary.

page 106

Same or Opposite

1. potential, possible
2. circuit, path
3. heat, warmth
4. power, electricity

Word Study

A. 1. electrical, connected to electricity
   2. figural, connected to a picture that shows information
   3. potential, something that is possible but isn't yet real
B. 1. figural
   2. potential
   3. electrical

page 107

Answers to restated questions will vary. Check students' responses.

1. C   2. C   3. A

page 108

Answers will vary.

page 109

1. B   6. B
2. B   7. D
3. C   8. B
4. D   9. C
5. A   10. D

page 112

1. gravity   4. motion
2. magnets   5. friction
3. position   6. force

page 113

Word Challenge:
True or False

1. T
2. F; If you had to move a large rock, you would need a lever.
3. F; Gravity causes objects to fall toward the ground when dropped.
4. F; When you apply your knowledge to solve a problem, you use what you have learned.

Word Challenge:
Which Word?

Answers will vary.

page 114

Extend the Meaning

1. b   3. c
2. a   4. b

Word Challenge:
What's Your Answer?

Answers will vary.

Word Study

A. 1. gravitation
   2. position
   3. application
B. 1. position
   2. application
   3. gravitation

page 115

Answers to restated questions will vary. Check students' responses.

1. B   2. A   3. B

page 116

Answers will vary.

page 117

1. C   6. B
2. B   7. D
3. A   8. C
4. D   9. B
5. C   10. C

page 120

1. lenses   5. absorb
2. rays   6. pitch
3. reflected   7. visible
4. prism   8. vibrate

page 121

Word Challenge:
Describe the Scene

Answers will vary.

Word Challenge:
Finish the Idea

Answers will vary.

page 122

Categories

Sound: absorb, pitch, reflect, vibrate

Light: absorb, lens, prism, ray, visible, reflect

Word Study

1. visual, relating to sight
2. visualize, to see
3. visibility, the state of being able to be seen
4. invisibility, the state of being unable to be seen

page 123

Answers to restated questions will vary. Check students' responses.

1. B   2. A   3. C

page 124

Answers will vary.

page 125

1. D   6. C
2. B   7. D
3. C   8. C
4. D   9. B
5. A   10. B

Vocabulary: Science, SV 9781419034992